Bricklaying

CONSTRUCTION SERIES

Bricklaying

CONSTRUCTION SERIES

skills2learn
www.skills2learn.com
Experts in e-learning & virtual reality simulation

CENGAGE
Learning™

Australia • Brazil • Japan • Korea • Mexico • Singapore • Spain • United Kingdom • United States

Bricklaying
Skills2Learn

Publishing Director: Linden Harris

Commissioning Editor: Lucy Mills

Development Editor: Helen Green

Editorial Assistant: Claire Napoli

Project Editor: Lucy Arthy

Production Controller: Eyvett Davis

Marketing Manager: Jason Bennett

Typesetter: MPS Limited, a Macmillan
   Company

Cover design: HCT Creative

Text design: Design Deluxe

For product information and technology assistance,
contact **emea.info@cengage.com.**

For permission to use material from this text or product,
and for permission queries,
email **emea.permissions@cengage.com.**

DISCLAIMER

This publication has been developed by Cengage Learning. It is intended as a method of studying and to assist in training in relation to its subject matter and should be used only as part of a comprehensive training programme with tutor guidance. Cengage Learning has taken all reasonable care in the preparation of this publication but Cengage learning and Skills2Learn and its partners accept no liability howsoever in respect of any breach of the rights of any third party howsoever occasioned or damage caused to any third party as a result of this publication. The information contained in the publication is not a substitute for manufacturer's guidelines or current legislation. Cengage Learning and Skills2Learn and its partners do not endorse or recommend any of the proprietary products that may be named in the publication.

British Library Cataloguing-in-Publication Data

A catalogue record for this book is available from the British Library.

ISBN: 978-1-4080-4185-7

Cengage Learning EMEA

Cheriton House, North Way, Andover, Hampshire, SP10 5BE
United Kingdom

Cengage Learning products are represented in Canada by Nelson Education Ltd.

For your lifelong learning solutions, visit **www.cengage.co.uk**

Purchase your next print book, e-book or e-chapter at **www.cengagebrain.com**

Printed in Malta by Melita Press
1 2 3 4 5 6 7 8 9 10 – 14 13 12

Contents

Foreword vi
About the Construction Consortia vii
About e-learning viii
About the NOS xiii
About the book xiv

1 Getting started 1

Introduction 2
Site analysis 5
Planning permission 7
Codes of practice 14
Check your knowledge 15

2 Materials 17

Bricks and blocks 18
Mortars 26
Cavity walls 37
Ordering of materials 43
Storage of materials 45
Disposal of waste 48
Check your knowledge 50

3 Setting out 51

Introduction 52
Profile boards 56
Setting up lines 58
Excavation 59
Concreting 60
Check your knowledge 65

4 Building below ground level 67

Foundations 68
Bonding 73
Brickwork to DPC 79
Types of flooring 87
Check your knowledge 90

5 Building above ground level 93

Dry bonding 94
Cavity walls 96
Jointing and pointing 100
Bridging openings 104
Internal walls 110
Joist hangers and gable ends 111
Checks 113
Check your knowledge 114

6 End test 117

End test objectives 117
The test 118

Answers to check your knowledge
    and end test 122
Glossary 128
Index 134

Foreword

The construction industry is a significant part of the UK economy and a major employer of people. It has a huge impact on the environment and plays a role in our everyday life in many ways. With environmental issues such as climate change and sustainable sourcing of materials now playing an important part in the design and construction of buildings and other structures, there is a need to educate and re-educate those new to the industry and those currently involved.

This construction series of e-learning programmes and text workbooks has been developed to provide a structured blended learning approach that will enhance the learning experience and stimulate a deeper understanding of the construction trades and give an awareness of sustainability issues. The content within these learning materials has been aligned to units of the Bricklaying, National Occupational Standards, and can be used as a support tool whilst studying for relevant vocational qualifications.

The uniqueness of this construction series is that it aims to bridge the gap between classroom-based and practical-based learning. The workbooks provide classroom-based activities that can involve learners in discussions and research tasks as well as providing them with understanding and knowledge of the subject. The e-learning programmes take the subject further, with high quality images, animations and audio further enhancing the content and showing information in a different light. In addition, the e-practical side of the e-learning places the learner in a virtual environment where they can move around freely, interact with objects and use the knowledge and skills they have gained from the workbook and e-learning to complete a set of tasks whilst in the comfort of a safe working environment.

The workbooks and e-learning programmes are designed to help learners continuously improve their skills and provide confidence and a sound knowledge base before getting their hands dirty in the real world.

About the Construction Consortia

This series of construction workbooks and e-learning programmes have been developed by the E-Construction Consortium. The consortium is a group of colleges and organizations that are passionate about the construction industry and are determined to enhance the learning experiences of people within the different trades or those that are new to it.

The consortium members have many years experience in the construction and educational sectors and have created this blended learning approach of interactive e-learning programmes and text workbooks to achieve the aim of:

- Providing accessible training in different areas of construction.
- Bridging the gap between classroom based and practical based learning.
- Providing a concentrated set of improvement learning modules.
- Enabling learners to gain new skills and qualifications more effectively.
- Improving functional skills and awareness of sustainability issues within the industry.
- Promoting health and safety in the industry.
- Encouraging training and continuous professional development.

For more information about this construction series please visit: **www.e-construction.co.uk** or **www.skills2learn.com**.

About e-learning

INTRODUCTION

This construction series of workbooks and e-learning programmes use a blended learning approach to train learners about construction skills. Blended learning allows training to be delivered through different mediums such as books, e-learning (computer-based training), practical workshops, and traditional classroom techniques. These training methods are designed to complement each other and work in tandem to achieve overall learning objectives and outcomes.

E-LEARNING

The Bricklaying e-learning programme that is also available to sit alongside this workbook offers a different method of learning. With technology playing an increasingly important part of everyday life, e-learning uses visually rich 2D and 3D graphics/animation, audio, video, text and interactive quizzes, to allow you to engage with the content and learn at your own pace and in your own time.

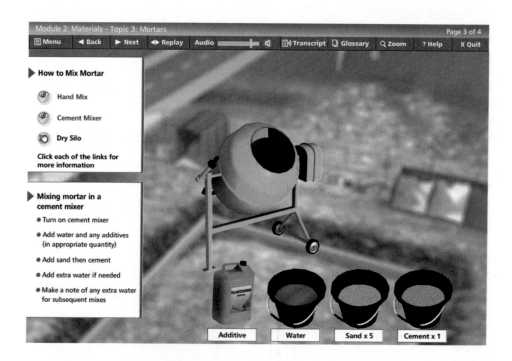

E-PRACTICAL

Part of the e-learning programme is an e-practical interactive scenario. This facility allows you to be immersed in a virtual reality situation where the choices you make affect the outcome. Using 3D technology, you can move freely around the environment, interact with objects, carry out tests, and make decisions and mistakes until you have mastered the subject. By practising in a virtual environment you will not only be able to see what you've learnt but also analyse your approach and thought process to the problem.

BENEFITS OF E-LEARNING

Diversity – E-Learning can be used for almost anything. With the correct approach any subject can be brought to life to provide an interactive training experience.

Technology – Advancements in computer technology now allow a wide range of spectacular and engaging e-learning to be delivered to a wider population.

Captivate and Motivate – Hold the learner's attention for longer with the use of high quality graphics, animation, sound and interactivity.

Safe Environment – E-Practical scenarios can create environments which simulate potentially harmful real-life situations or replicate a piece of dangerous equipment, therefore allowing the learner to train and gain experience and knowledge in a completely safe environment.

Instant Feedback – Learners can undertake training assessments which feedback results instantly. This can provide information on where they need to re-study or congratulate them on passing the assessment. Results and Certificates can also be printed for future records.

On-Demand – Can be accessed 24 hours a day, 7 days a week, 365 days of the year. You can access the content at any time and view it at your own pace.

Portable Solutions – Can be delivered via a CD, website or LMS. Learners no longer need to travel to all lectures, conferences, meetings or training days. This saves many man-hours in reduced travelling, cost of hotels and expenses amongst other things.

Reduction of Costs – Can be used to teach best practice processes on jobs which use large quantities or expensive materials. Learners can practise their techniques and boost their confidence to a high enough standard before being allowed near real materials.

BRICKLAYING E-LEARNING

The aim of the bricklaying e-learning programme is to enhance a learner's knowledge and understanding of the bricklaying trade. The course content is aligned to units from the bricklaying Trowel Occupations; National Occupational Standards (NOS) so can be used for study towards certification.

The programme gives the learners an understanding of the technicalities of bricklaying as well as looking at sustainability, health and safety and functional skills in an interactive and visually engaging manner. It also provides a 'real-life' scenario where the learner can apply the knowledge gained from the tutorials in a safe yet practical way.

By using and completing this programme, it is expected that learners will:

- Be able to explain the preliminary works carried out prior to the start of any bricklaying
- Understand the role of the bricklayer in the working environment and have knowledge of some of the tools that will be used
- Be able to explain the choice of materials for a project, calculate the correct quantities, source these from an appropriate supplier and identify the correct disposal method for waste materials
- Understand the processes involved in setting out the structure on the site
- Understand the different types of foundations, bondings and floorings
- Understand the construction of brickwork including the internal structure, the cavity and the external structure

The e-learning programme is divided into the following learning modules:

- Getting Started
- Materials
- Setting Out
- Building Below Ground Level
- Building Above Ground Level
- End Test
- Interactive E-Practical Scenario

THE CONSTRUCTION SERIES

As part of the construction series the following e-learning programmes and workbooks are available. For more information please contact the sales team on **emea.fesales@cengage.com** or visit the website **www.e-construction.co.uk**.

- Plastering
- Bricklaying
- Carpentry & Joinery
- Painting & Decorating
- Wall & Floor Tiling

About the NOS

The National Occupational Standards (NOS) provide a framework of information that outline the skills, knowledge and understanding required to carry out work-based activities within a given vocation. Each standard is divided into units that cover specific activities of that occupation. Employers, employees, teachers and learners can use these standards as information, support and a reference resource that will enable them to understand the skills and criteria required for good practice in the workplace.

The standards are used as a basis to develop many vocational qualifications in the United Kingdom for a wide range of occupations. This workbook and associated e-learning programme are aligned to the Bricklaying Trowel Occupations, National Occupational Standards, and the information within relates to the following units:

- Conform to General Workplace Safety
- Move and Handle Resources
- Prepare and Mix Concrete and Mortars
- Lay Bricks and Blocks to Line
- Contribute to Setting Out Basic Masonry Structures
- Joint Brick and Block Structures
- Erect Masonry Structures
- Erect Thin Joint Masonry Structures
- Place and Finish Non-Specialist Concrete
- Set Out Complex Masonry Structures
- Repair and Maintain Masonry Structures
- Develop and Maintain Good Working Relationships
- Confirm the Occupational Method of Work

About the book

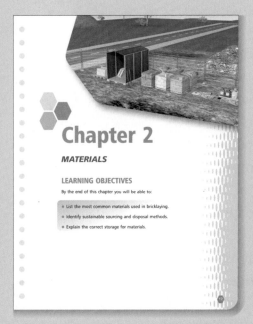

Learning Objectives at the start of each chapter explain the skills and knowledge you need to be proficient in and understand by the end of the chapter.

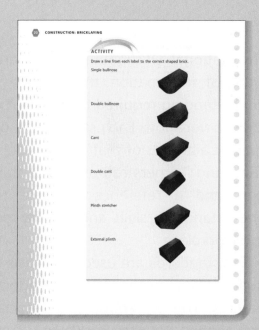

Activities are practical tasks that engage you in the subject and further your understanding.

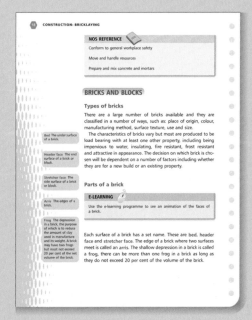

E-Learning Icons link the workbook content to the e-learning programme.

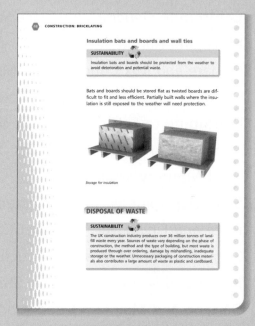

Sustainability Boxes provide information and helpful advice on how to work in a sustainable and environmentally friendly way.

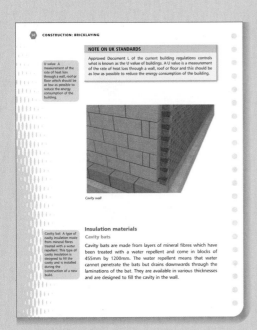

Note on UK Standards draws your attention to relevant building regulations.

Functional Skills Icons highlight activities that develop and test your Maths, English and ICT key skills.

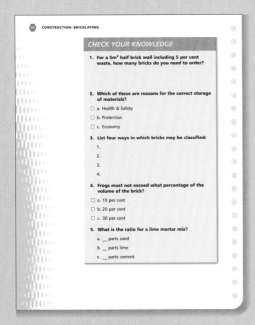

Check Your Knowledge at the end of each chapter to test your knowledge and understanding.

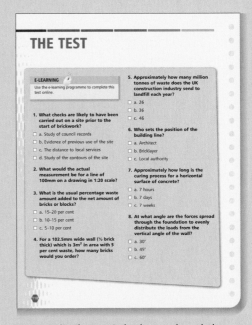

End Test in Chapter 6 checks your knowledge on all the information within the workbook.

Chapter 1

GETTING STARTED

LEARNING OBJECTIVES

By the end of this chapter you will be able to:

- Understand what a bricklayer does and identify the skills required to be a bricklayer.

- Explain what site analysis has been carried out prior to the start of bricklaying.

- Understand what **planning permissions** have been granted to the site.

- List the codes of practice applicable to the work to be carried out.

Planning permission Application to the local councils for land to be developed or addition/modification made to an existing property.

Trowel A range of hand-held tools used for mix, apply and spread or remove materials. There are many different types of trowels for different purposes including bucket trowel, gauge trowel, notched trowel and pointing trowel.

Block The most common block type is aggregate concrete blocks. They have a large number of desirable properties including high sound and thermal insulation and excellent moisture, fire and frost resistance. They are strong, lightweight, easy to work with and easy to fix to. Blocks are manufactured in solid, hollow and cellular block forms and one type of block can be used in every situation on a site.

Course A row of bricks, concrete blocks, etc. in a wall.

Level The horizontal level of a surface or structure.

Plumb The vertical level of a surface or structure.

NOS REFERENCE

Develop and maintain good working relationships

Confirm the occupational method of work

INTRODUCTION

The role of the bricklayer

The bricklayer has a number of roles including:

- Building the interior and exterior walls of new buildings.
- Repairing existing walls.
- Refurbishing old buildings.

All of these roles include cutting bricks manually or with portable power tools, spreading mortar with **trowels**, laying bricks and **blocks** in **courses** and checking that the wall is straight, **level** and **plumb** of vertical. Bricklayers can work for a number of employers including private households, building contractors, local authorities or specialist contractors.

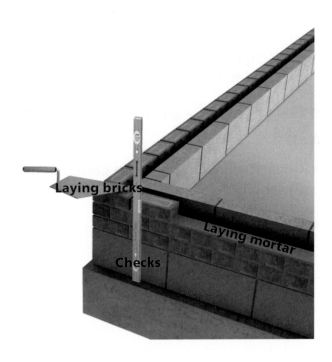

Skills required by a bricklayer

JOB VACANCY

Job Title:
Bricklayer

Location:
Nationwide

Hours:
Average 37.5 hours
per week

Work Pattern:
Monday to Friday

Skills Required:
- Fit and healthy
- Practical ability
- Head for heights
- Planning skills
- Multi-tasking
- Team player
- Aptitude for maths
- Working safely
- Follow instructions

NOTE ON UK STANDARDS

It is possible to train as a bricklayer at any age. Most people train on the job as well as attending a college or training centre to gain qualifications or train through a Modern Apprenticeship or Construction Apprenticeship. Experienced bricklayers may choose to specialize in areas such as restoration and conservation, or progress to construction management.

HEALTH & SAFETY

Complete the following Activity on Personal Protective Equipment.

ACTIVITY

When working on site you must follow all health and safety procedures and guidelines. You will need to wear all the necessary **Personal Protective Equipment (PPE)** and know what to do in case of an emergency. Find the following words associated with health and safety in the grid below.

I	E	T	D	U	T	G	F	E	O	T	P	N	A	T	E	S
A	O	M	U	O	L	Y	A	F	S	G	O	G	G	L	E	S
E	E	L	I	O	H	R	I	E	A	M	S	G	C	A	G	T
K	E	O	V	M	M	Y	V	I	T	S	I	A	A	T	Q	A
O	N	E	E	U	W	S	R	O	S	N	M	H	T	O	R	H
O	S	E	F	T	I	D	F	I	E	O	G	T	V	O	I	D
L	E	F	E	V	S	T	O	O	B	Y	T	E	F	A	S	R
L	S	R	H	P	N	H	T	T	D	A	R	C	E	M	O	A
P	P	G	T	S	A	R	T	R	D	A	R	A	T	T	A	H
C	I	C	D	E	A	D	E	F	L	C	A	Y	R	T	P	K
H	I	N	E	O	Y	T	S	L	E	Y	E	W	A	S	H	S
U	D	O	T	Y	H	F	S	E	E	E	R	V	D	M	F	A
H	Y	W	E	C	U	W	U	S	A	D	D	C	N	N	H	M
O	O	R	F	N	S	I	H	C	O	F	E	I	I	T	S	T
R	E	H	S	I	U	G	N	I	T	X	E	E	R	I	F	S
T	I	K	D	I	A	T	S	R	I	F	T	E	S	R	H	U
O	M	F	T	N	S	P	I	T	T	M	I	S	U	F	O	D

GLOVES, GOGGLES, HARD HAT, HIGH VIS VEST, DUST MASK, BOOTS, KNEE PADS, EAR MUFFS, OVERALLS, FIRST AID KIT, EYE WASH, FIRE EXTINGUISHER

Building design

Each building job will have a design specification document and a bill of quantities. These documents will contain:

- Detailed plans of the build.
- Information on how the construction should be built.
- A list of materials that need to be used and their quantities.

NOTE ON UK STANDARDS

These documents will be required to satisfy and comply with building regulations and meet the approval of local authorities. You will need to refer to and understand these documents to make sure the building is constructed correctly.

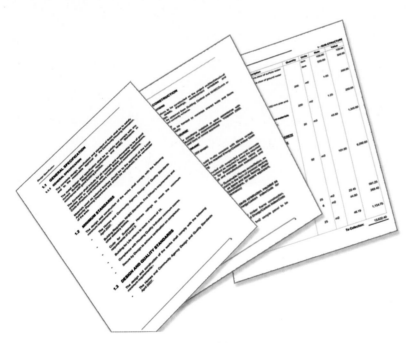

Design specifications and bill of quantities

SITE ANALYSIS

Introduction to site analysis

Prior to any work taking place, a detailed analysis of the site is carried out. Study of the history of the land in council records will establish whether the site is a greenfield or brownfield site. The records also show the location of any existing services, as well as evidence of potential problems of previous use, such as old foundations, wells and tipping operations. It will establish whether the site is within a conservation area or close to listed buildings and a study of geographical maps will show the contours and make up of the land. Finally, any regeneration grants and tax incentives are researched.

Analysis of the site is required

The bricklayer on site

Bricklayers are generally one of the first trades on site once the site has been cleared. On larger sites, designers and engineers set out the positioning of the walls and the bricklayer may have to lay several hundred bricks a day as part of a team working on different sections of a building at the same time. On a smaller site the bricklayer may need to set out the site, carry his own bricks and mix his own mortar.

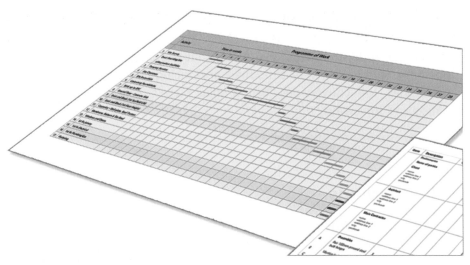

Example of work documents

NOTE ON UK STANDARDS

Usually bricklayers are required to work approximately 37.5 hours from Monday to Friday. This can vary to take advantage of daylight hours or to avoid disrupting business, and overtime at weekends or in the evening is common.

PLANNING PERMISSION

When to apply

Before you arrive on site, planning permission will have been granted for the proposed building. Planning permission is not always required and advice on when planning permission is needed can be found on the planning portal website or from the planning department of your local council. In order to apply for planning permission, detailed drawings need to be submitted.

ACTIVITY

Use a search engine to find the planning portal website and make a note of the web address below.

_____

NOTE ON UK STANDARDS

In October 2008, the rules for projects that can be carried out without planning permission were simplified and include extensions and conservatories, loft conversions, fitting solar panels, roof alterations and patios and driveways.

FUNCTIONAL SKILLS

Scale drawings

It would be impractical to produce building drawings to their full size so they are reduced to a ratio of the real size, known as a scale drawing. For example, in a drawing to a scale of 1:10, 100mm will represent 1000mm or 1m, and on a scale 1:100, 100mm will represent 10,000mm or 10m. This means that in order to calculate the actual measurement from the scale drawing you multiply the scale measurement by the scale ratio.

British standards A set of standards to ensure the quality of goods and services.

NOTE ON UK STANDARDS

All construction drawings are produced in accordance with **British Standard** 1192 Drawing Office Practice.

E-LEARNING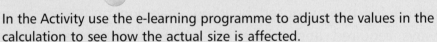

In the Activity use the e-learning programme to adjust the values in the calculation to see how the actual size is affected.

ACTIVITY

FUNCTIONAL SKILLS

What measurement would 100mm represent in each of the following scales? Enter the values below:

    1:2500 –

    1:500 –

    1:200 –

    1:20 –

Types of drawing

There are a number of different types of drawing that are produced as part of what are known as 'working drawings'.

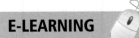

E-LEARNING

Use the e-learning programme to see more detailed drawings.

Block plans

Block plans are used to identify the site in relation to the surrounding area and are usually produced in 1:2500 scale. They are very small and do not allow for much more than an outline of the site and its boundaries. The orientation of the site is shown with an appropriate logo.

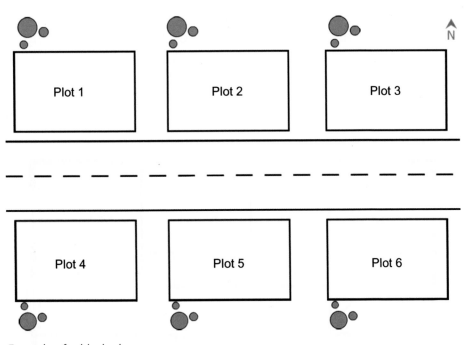

Example of a block plan

Site plan

The site plan shows the position of the proposed building on the site as well as proposed roads, drainage and service layouts. They are usually produced in 1:500 scale and again the orientation should be included.

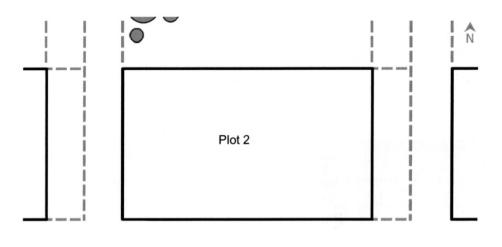

Example of a site plan

Plan drawing

Plan drawings show a bird's-eye view of a building including all rooms, windows and doors. They are produced in 1:200 scale and usually match the elevation drawings.

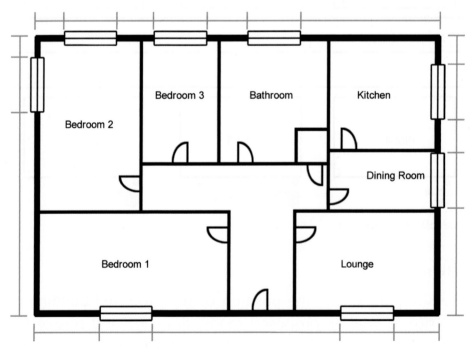

Example of a plan drawing

Elevation drawing

Elevation drawings show the exterior of a building from all sides and include all measurements.

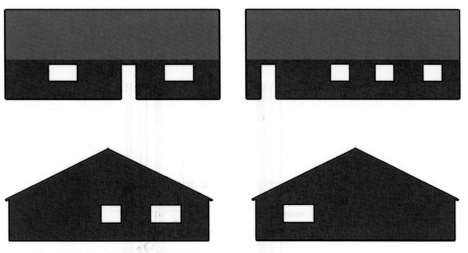

Example of an elevation drawing

Cross section drawing

Cross section drawings show details that would not show on plan and elevation drawings. A scale is chosen to show information that could not be included in other drawings.

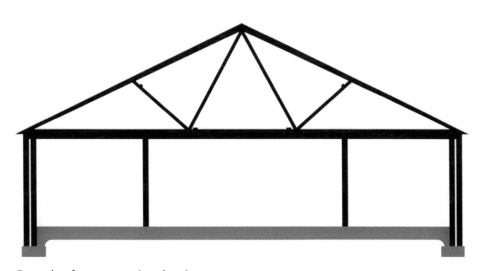

Example of a cross section drawing

Assembly drawing

Assembly drawings show the detailed information at the junction between different elements and components of a building. These are very important drawings and show exactly how the architect wants the building to be constructed and what materials should be used. They are produced in 1:20 scale.

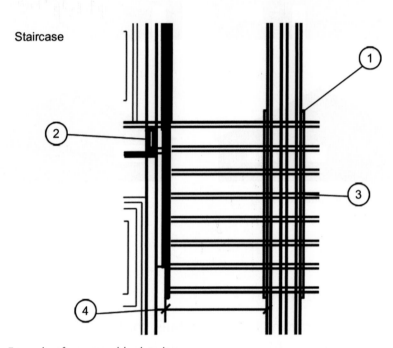

Example of an assembly drawing

ACTIVITY

What does your home look like? Try drawing plan and elevation diagrams of your house.

CODES OF PRACTICE

The Approved Code of Practice (ACoP)

NOTE ON UK STANDARDS

The Approved Code of Practice, or ACoP, has special legal status and gives practical advice for all those involved in construction work. This includes:

- The legal duties placed on clients, designers, contractors and workers.
- Information on the new role of Construction Design and Management coordinator or CDM.
- Which construction projects need to be notified to the Health and Safety Executive before work starts and gives information on how this should be done.
- How to assess the competence of organizations and individuals involved in construction work.
- How to improve the cooperation and coordination between all those involved within the construction project and what essential information needs to be recorded in construction health and safety plans and files.

ACTIVITY

Use a search engine to find the Approved Code of Practice website and make a note of the web address below.

_____

Regulations

NOTE ON UK STANDARDS

The Construction Design and Management Regulations were updated in 2007. Everyone in construction needs to know about these regulations in order to:

- Improve health and safety in the industry.
- Have the right people for the right job at the right time.
- Manage the risks on site.
- Focus on effective planning.

ACTIVITY

Use a search engine to find details of the Construction Design and Management Regulations (CDM 2007) and make a note of the web address below.

_____

CHECK YOUR KNOWLEDGE

1. **True or False: As the bricklayer on site, it is your responsibility to carry out a site analysis before starting work.**

   ☐ a. True

   ☐ b. False

2. **True or False: Planning permission is required for every type of building work.**

   ☐ a. True

   ☐ b. False

3. **True or False: Bricklayers can only work for a site contractor.**

☐ a. True

☐ b. False

4. **If a 100mm line on a drawing represents 1000mm or 1m on site, which scale is being used?**

☐ a. 1:10

☐ b. 1:100

☐ c. 1:1000

5. **When were the CDM Regulations updated?**

☐ a. 2005

☐ b. 2006

☐ c. 2007

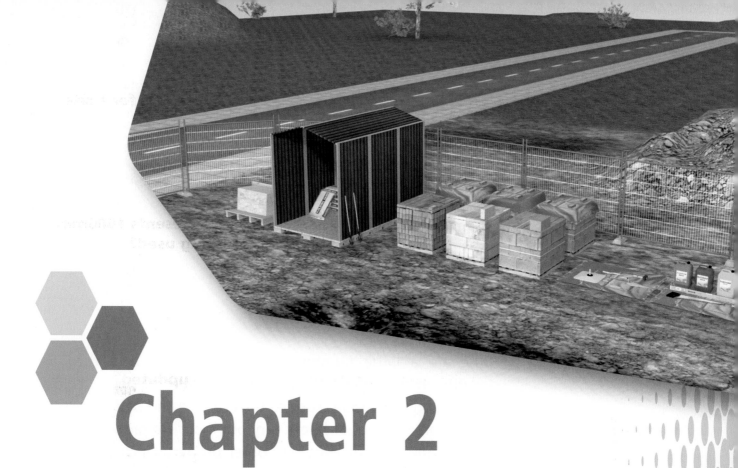

Chapter 2

MATERIALS

LEARNING OBJECTIVES

By the end of this chapter you will be able to:

- List the most common materials used in bricklaying.

- Identify sustainable sourcing and disposal methods.

- Explain the correct storage for materials.

NOS REFERENCE

Conform to general workplace safety

Move and handle resources

Prepare and mix concrete and mortars

BRICKS AND BLOCKS

Types of bricks

There are a large number of bricks available and they are classified in a number of ways, such as: place of origin, colour, manufacturing method, surface texture, use and size.

The characteristics of bricks vary but most are produced to be load bearing with at least one other property, including being impervious to water, insulating, fire resistant, frost resistant and attractive in appearance. The decision on which brick is chosen will be dependent on a number of factors including whether they are for a new build or an existing property.

Parts of a brick

E-LEARNING

Use the e-learning programme to see an animation of the faces of a brick.

Bed The under surface of a brick.

Header face The end surface of a brick or block.

Stretcher face The side surface of a brick or block.

Arris The edges of a brick.

Frog The depression in a brick, the purpose of which is to reduce the amount of clay used in manufacture and its weight. A brick may have two frogs but must not exceed 20 per cent of the net volume of the brick.

Each surface of a brick has a set name. These are **bed**, **header face** and **stretcher face**. The edge of a brick where two surfaces meet is called an **arris**. The shallow depression in a brick is called a **frog**, there can be more than one frog in a brick as long as they do not exceed 20 per cent of the volume of the brick.

ACTIVITY

Label each of the surfaces of the brick shown.

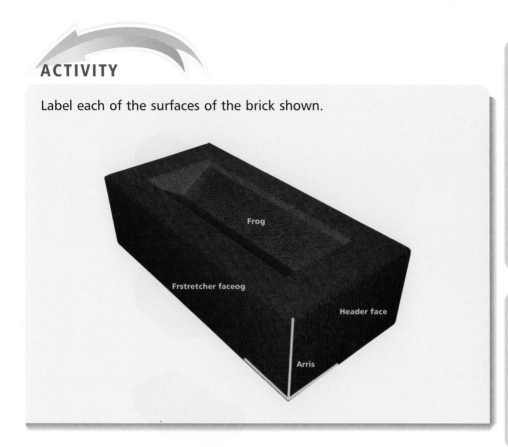

Brick shapes

As well as standard bricks, there are also a number of special shaped bricks that are designed to suit a wide range of construction projects and situations. These include single and double **bullnose bricks**, **cant** and double cant bricks and **plinth stretcher** and **external plinth** bricks.

Bullnose brick A type of cut brick. These may be single or double bullnose. Either one or two ends of the stretcher face will have a 56mm radius curve. The single bullnose is used on the edges of sills or steps and is flat to form a radius corner. The double bullnose is used on edge as a capping brick.

Cant brick A type of cut brick. These may be single or double bull cant. Either one or two ends of the stretcher face will have a 45° cut. The uses of these bricks are similar to those for bullnose bricks.

Plinth stretcher A facing brick with a 45° chamfer on the stretcher face used to reduce the thickness of a plinth by 56mm (quarter brick).

External plinth A facing brick with a 45° chamfer on the header and stretcher faces used to reduce the thickness of a plinth by 56mm (quarter brick) per course.

ACTIVITY

Draw a line from each label to the correct shaped brick.

Single bullnose

Double bullnose

Cant

Double cant

Plinth stretcher

External plinth

Calculating quantities of bricks

E-LEARNING

Use the e-learning programme to see an animated explanation of this calculation.

When calculating the number of bricks for a project you first need to know the surface area of the stretcher face of one brick.

FUNCTIONAL SKILLS

Standard bricks are 215mm long and 65mm high. 10mm is added to both of these measurements to allow for joints so the accepted measurement is 225mm long and 75mm high.	225mm × 75mm
If we multiply 225mm by 75mm we get a surface area of 0.01688m^2 which we will round up to 0.0169m^2.	225mm × 75mm = 0.01688m^2 (rounded up to 0.0169m^2)
We now need to calculate the number of bricks needed per m^2 of wall which we do by dividing 1m by the surface area of the brick. 1m divided by 0.0169 gives us 59.17 bricks which we will round up to 60.	1.000 ÷ 0.0169 = 59.17 (rounded up to 60)
We now know we need 60 bricks per m^2 of wall which applies when the wall is built as a half brick wall. This means the bricks are laid lengthwise so the wall is half a brick thick. For a 1 brick wall we would need twice as many bricks and for a 1½ brick wall we would need 180 bricks per m^2 of wall.	1 brick thick = 120 bricks per m^2 of wall 1½ brick thick = 180 bricks per m^2 of wall

Standard brick measurements

Standard brick measurements with mortar

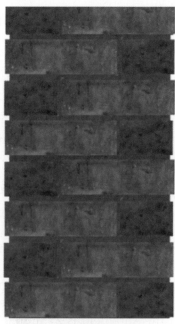

½ brick thick wall   1 brick thick wall   1½ brick thick wall

ACTIVITY

How many bricks would you need for a 1 brick thick 2m² wall?
   Show your working out below.

Types of blocks

Aggregate concrete blocks have a large number of desirable properties including high sound and thermal insulation as well as excellent moisture, fire and frost resistance.

They are strong, lightweight, easy to work with and easy to fix to. This has made them the most commonly used block type in the construction industry. Blocks are manufactured in solid, hollow and cellular block forms and one type of block can be used in every situation on a site.

> **Aggregate** The name given to the range of particulates used in construction. These can include sand, gravel and crushed stone.

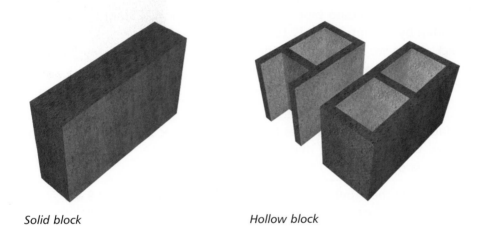

Solid block   *Hollow block*

Cellular block

Calculating quantities of blocks

FUNCTIONAL SKILLS

The calculations for blocks are very similar to the calculations for bricks.

The face of a standard block is 440mm by 215mm and it is 100mm thick. Again we add 10mm to these numbers to allow for joints, making the face of the block 450mm by 225mm.	450mm × 225mm
Using the same calculation as for bricks, we can work out that the surface area of a block is 0.10125m².	450mm × 225mm = 0.10125m²
To calculate the number of blocks needed per m² of wall we divide 1m by the surface area of the block. In this case 1m divided by 0.10125 gives us 9.87 blocks which we will round up to 10. We now know we need 10 blocks per m² of wall.	1.000 ÷ 0.10125 = 9.87 (rounded up to 10)

Standard block measurements

Standard block measurements with mortar

ACTIVITY

How many blocks would you need for a 2m² wall?
Show your working out below.

HEALTH & SAFETY

There are a number of health and safety issues that are specific to working with bricks. When cutting bricks, eye injuries can be caused from flying fragments of brick, the use of safety goggles will eliminate this risk.

Dust exposure when cutting bricks can lead to silicosis, an occupational lung disease caused by the inhalation of silica dust. Using a block splitter instead of an angle grinder can significantly reduce the amount of dust produced and water spray to damp down the dust on a regular basis can also help. Where the risk is greatest, a respirator should be worn. Gloves should be worn when working with bricks and blocks to reduce associated risks such as cuts and abrasions.

ACTIVITY

Can you draw some of the health & safety signs you may see on a building site?

Wear head protection sign

Wear dust mask sign

Foot protection sign

Hearing protection sign

Sand Fine aggregate that is one of the raw ingredients for mixing mortar.

Cement A grey or white powdery material made from chalk or limestone and clay. Cement is the most common binder in bricklaying mortar and works by hardening as a result of a chemical reaction when mixed with water.

Plasticizer An additive that increases fluidity or plasticity of a mortar, cement paste or concrete mixture and reduces water content and drying times.

Retarder An additive used to extend the setting time of a mortar mix.

Accelerator An additive that speeds up the hydration of cement producing a higher strength at an earlier stage which reduces the setting time.

MORTARS

Materials used in mortar

Mortar is the material used to bed, joint and point bricks and blocks in walling. It can consist of **sand**, **cement**, water, **plasticizer**, **retarder**, **accelerator** and lime. The aim of the mix is to produce a workable mortar which is described as 'fatty'. This means it sticks to the trowel without being too sticky, spreads easily and does not dry too quickly or too slowly.

The other properties that are required of mortar are:

- sufficient compressive strength
- sufficient bond strength
- durability
- an attractive appearance.

Sand

Sand for mortar should be clean and free from impurities such as salt. It should be well graded with a good mix of fine, medium and coarse particles and should be able to pass through a 5mm sieve. Poorly graded sand contains a larger volume of air and will be weaker and more likely to shrink, leaving cracks where rain can penetrate.

Cement

Cement is the most common binder in bricklaying mortar and the most commonly used cement is **Ordinary Portland Cement** or **OPC**. It sets into a solid mass when mixed with water.

Water

Water is used to mix mortar, it must be clean otherwise it may affect the strength of the mortar when it dries.

Plasticizer

Plasticizers improve the workability of a mortar mix but should not be used in structural work without the permission of the structural engineer.

Retarder

Retarders extend the setting time of a mortar mix.

Accelerator

Accelerators speed up the hydration of cement producing a higher strength at an earlier stage which reduces the setting time. However, they can be corrosive to steel and care should be taken where the mortar may come into contact with any steel reinforcement.

Lime

There are two types of **lime**, hydraulic and non-hydraulic. They can both be used for mortar and **pointing**. The difference is in the setting time. Production and sustainability benefits make lime an eco-friendly material.

Ordinary Portland Cement (OPC) The most common type of cement. Made from crushed limestone or clay mixed with water, which is then heated at very high temperatures and ground into a powder form.

Lime A white or grayish-white, odorless solid made from calcium carbonate, limestone or oyster shells. Used in mortars, plasters and cements.

Pointing Finishing off mortar joints that have been raked out to a depth of between 15–20mm. Pointing can be carried out during construction to apply a different colour mortar to contrast the brickwork, or it can be part of a renovation project if existing mortar has deteriorated.

Ratio for a lime mortar mix = 6 parts sand, 1 part lime and 1 part cement.

Some of the materials used in mortar

Mortar mixes

The ingredients of a mortar mix have to be measured in the correct proportions before the mortar can actually be mixed and are measured either by weight or volume. The table shows the mix proportions used for bricks and blocks in the average strength category above and below ground.

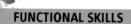

FUNCTIONAL SKILLS

Mortar mix (by volume)	Ratio	Use
Masonry cement and sand	1: (4 to 5)	Below DPC level Bricks and blocks with average strength
Cement: sand with plasticizer	1: (5 to 6)	Below DPC level Bricks and blocks with average strength
Masonry cement and sand	1: (5.5 to 6.5)	Above DPC level Bricks and blocks with average strength
Cement: sand with plasticizer	1: (7 to 8)	Above DPC level Bricks and blocks with average strength

For example, a mix of masonry cement and sand for bricks and blocks in the average strength category for use below ground would have a mix of one part cement to four to five parts sand.

Water is then added to produce a 'fatty' mix. The amount of water added directly affects the strength of the mortar, which should approximately match the strength of the brick or block it is being used with. Under no circumstances should the mortar be stronger than the brick or block.

ACTIVITY

If you are making a mortar mix to be used with bricks and blocks within the average strength category below **DPC** level with a ratio of 1:5 and are using 12kg of cement, how many kilograms of sand do you need?

Show your working out below.

DPC The standard and widely used abbreviation for damp proof course.

How to mix mortar

Mortar can be mixed by hand, in a cement mixer or supplied in a dry silo.

When mortar is mixed by hand, all the dry ingredients should be thoroughly combined before the water is added. The water should be poured carefully into a well made in the middle of the dry ingredients. The mortar is then mixed with a spade and should finish as an even colour.

Start with the cement

Add sand and mix through

Add water into a well-shaped hole

Mix materials thoroughly

Finished fatty mix

When using a cement mixer to make mortar, the mixer needs to be turned on before any materials are added. The water is added first, and if any **additives** such as a plasticizer are needed, then the appropriate amount is added to the water at this stage.

Next to be added is the sand, followed by the cement. Extra water can be added if needed but a mortar mix in a cement mixer will always appear dryer than it actually is. If extra water is used, the quantity should be noted so that subsequent mixes are identical.

Add the water

Add the sand

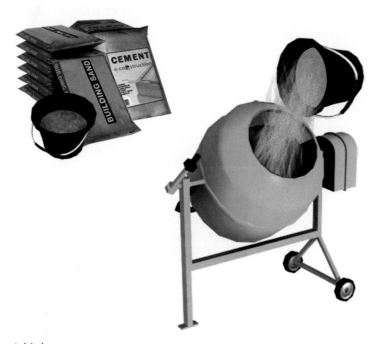

Add the cement

Your finished mix

Dry mortar silos can be placed on site and provide an efficient and protected way of providing mortar. The silo contains sand and cement materials ready mixed to the correct proportions, consistency and colour for the requirements of the job. When required, water is added and the mortar mix is produced. The benefits include accurate mix quantities with little wastage and reduced time and labour costs.

Dry silo container

ACTIVITY

In what order do you add materials to a mortar mix? Write the number order on the diagram below.

Hand mixing	
1	
2	
3	

Cement

Sand

Water

Cement mixer	
1	
2	
3	

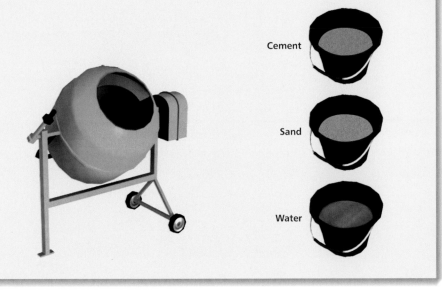

Cement

Sand

Water

E-LEARNING

Use the e-learning programme to read this information in a flip book.

HEALTH & SAFETY

When working with materials, tools and equipment, you should always take the necessary health and safety precautions. Here are some things you should be aware of:

- Direct skin contact with mortar can cause **dermatitis** and burns and measures should be put in place to stop this happening.

- Cement and products containing cement should be used within the use-by date.

- The risk of dermatitis and burns should be explained to all workers on a site.

- Direct skin contact with mortar should be avoided and CE-marked PVC gloves should be used as well as a barrier cream if available.

- Washing facilities including hot and cold water, soap and large enough basins should be provided on site.

- Supervisors should be aware of the early signs of dermatitis.

- The main contractor's first aid kit should include emergency eyewash.

- Training on how to treat exposure to mortar should be given to all workers.

Dermatitis A skin condition caused by direct skin contact with irritants (e.g. mortar mix) causing an allergic reaction.

ACTIVITY

Find the following words associated with bricklaying materials in the grid below.

E	S	R	N	Y	R	T	P	S	L	I	Y	E	P	A
E	Q	B	N	A	E	Q	N	K	L	D	T	X	P	C
I	U	Y	Y	J	H	T	A	E	V	J	P	T	I	C
D	M	V	E	U	C	N	G	R	M	F	B	E	C	E
O	E	C	K	E	T	S	G	E	E	E	I	R	L	L
U	M	G	W	B	E	I	R	D	S	T	C	N	T	E
W	I	T	D	Y	R	A	E	R	O	D	J	A	R	R
P	L	S	S	E	T	T	G	A	N	S	O	L	T	A
V	K	A	T	Y	S	M	A	T	L	O	L	P	W	T
W	N	I	L	C	H	K	T	E	L	N	C	L	A	O
D	S	X	X	M	T	P	E	R	U	V	T	I	Y	R
X	Y	Z	M	R	N	R	S	K	B	J	N	N	Q	T
R	E	Z	I	C	I	T	S	A	L	P	A	T	F	P
J	W	S	H	U	L	G	K	N	J	C	C	H	S	P
P	E	C	J	V	P	D	A	P	N	H	Y	V	G	X

ACCELERATOR, LIME, AGGREGATE, PLASTICIZER, BULLNOSE, PLINTH STRETCHER, CANT, RETARDER, CEMENT, SAND, EXTERNAL PLINTH

CAVITY WALLS

Cavity walls are designed to keep the inside of a building dry and to balance the temperature inside the building, keeping it warm in winter and cool in summer. There are three main types of **cavity insulation** materials.

Cavity The gap between the internal and external walls of a building. Usually 50mm wide to increase the thermal insulation and weather resistance of the wall. The cavity must be kept clear and not bridged (except for wall ties and insulation). A damp proof course (DPC) must be provided around the perimeter of openings in cavity walls otherwise dampness can occur internally.

Cavity insulation For new build the standard of thermal insulation for external walls, set by building regulations, requires a suitable insulating material to be fixed in the cavity. There are a number of products available, rigid or flexible, and these either partially or completely fill the cavity. For existing buildings with cavity walls, the insulation material is injected into and will completely fill the cavity.

NOTE ON UK STANDARDS

Approved Document L of the current building regulations controls what is known as the **U value** of buildings. A U value is a measurement of the rate of heat loss through a wall, roof or floor and this should be as low as possible to reduce the energy consumption of the building.

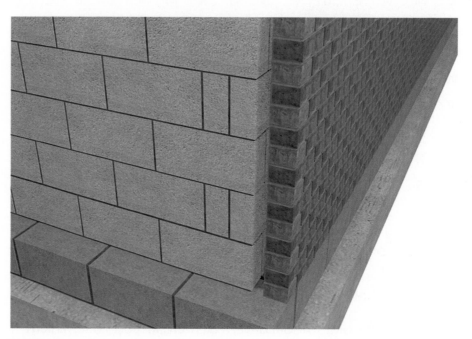

Cavity wall

Insulation materials

Cavity bats

Cavity bats are made from layers of mineral fibres which have been treated with a water repellent and come in blocks of 455mm by 1200mm. The water repellent means that water cannot penetrate the bats but drains downwards through the laminations of the bat. They are available in various thicknesses and are designed to fill the cavity in the wall.

Cavity wall with bats

Cavity board

Cavity boards can be made from a number of materials such as polyurethane, fibre glass and polystyrene and are supplied as rigid boards. They are designed to fix flat to the **inner leaf** of the wall and only partially fill the cavity.

Cavity wall with boards

Cavity board A type of cavity insulation made from polyurethane, fibre glass and polystyrene supplied as rigid boards. This type of cavity insulation is designed to partially fill the cavity and is installed during the construction of a new build.

Inner leaf The internal wall of a cavity construction which is commonly formed of blocks. If partial fill insulation cavity boards are used, they should be fixed to the inner leaf using special wall ties.

Cavity foam

Insulation can be injected into a wall after it is built making it a useful option for existing buildings as well as new builds. The insulation can be expanded foam (**cavity foam**), granules or mineral wool fibres and is designed to completely fill the cavity.

> **Cavity foam** A type of cavity insulation made from expanded foam, granules or mineral wool fibres. This type of cavity insulation is designed to fill the cavity and is injected into the cavity after a wall is constructed. Generally used for existing buildings with cavity walls.

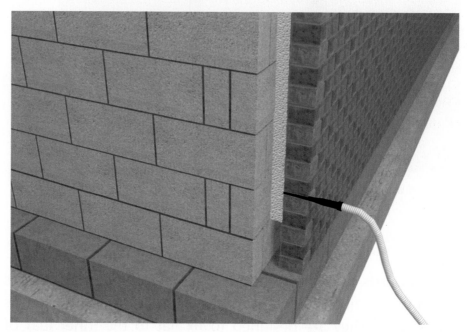

Cavity wall with foam

Wall ties

Wall ties are necessary to tie the two halves of a wall together and stop one moving independently of the other. The type of wall tie and the spacing between them will depend on a number of factors including:

> **Wall ties** Metal connectors built into cavity walls to provide a structural link between the inner and outer leaf of the wall. There are many different types of wall ties and some are specially designed for use with insulation materials.

- the brick and block type
- the width of the cavity
- the building type and location.

Wall ties should be placed level or even sloping towards the outside of the building to avoid damp being able to penetrate to the interior of the building. Ties should also be cleared of any mortar droppings which may form a bridge across the cavity and allow damp to travel to the inside wall.

A selection of wall ties

ACTIVITY

Draw on the diagram to show how wall ties should be positioned.

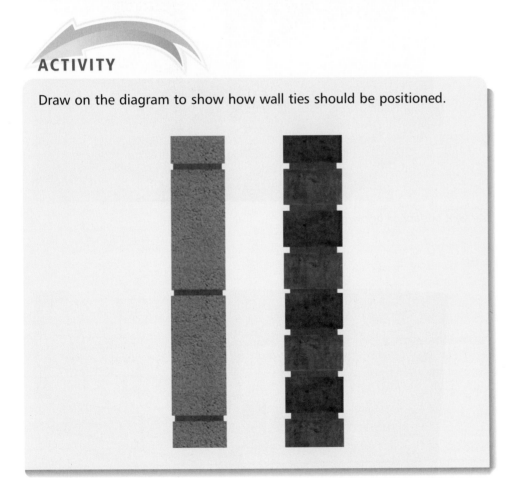

Air vents

E-LEARNING

Use the e-learning programme to see an animation of air vents in action.

Air vent Vents that can be built into a cavity wall below ground and above ground. Below ground they provide air where a hollow floor, normally of a timber construction, needs to be ventilated. Above ground they are built into the cavity where additional ventilation is needed in a room. Air vents bridge the cavity as a continuous duct to join the inlet and outlet of the openings.

Air vents can be built into a cavity wall below ground and above ground. Below ground they provide air where a hollow floor, normally of a timber construction, needs to be ventilated. Above ground they are built into the cavity where additional ventilation is needed in a room. Air vents bridge the cavity as a continuous duct to join the inlet and outlet of the openings.

Air vent positioned below ground

Air vent positioned above ground

When working on a renovation project, the bricklayer should be aware of the health and safety issues associated with **asbestos** insulating board. It was used as fireproofing material in a number of situations until the mid-1980s and releases fibres into the air when disturbed. Although use peaked in the 1960s and 1970s, any building that was constructed or had major renovation work carried out between the 1950s and mid 1980s is likely to contain some asbestos material of some kind. Work on asbestos insulating board normally needs a Health and Safety Executive licensed contractor.

Asbestos A fibrous mineral commonly used in buildings as fireproofing material until the mid 1980s. Can be a health hazard and should not be disturbed. Specialist advice must be sought if found or suspected.

ORDERING OF MATERIALS

Sourcing materials

SUSTAINABILITY

Ordering building materials from local suppliers contributes to lower carbon emission levels by reducing the carbon miles involved in transporting the materials, and you may also save on packaging and shipping costs. Apparent cost savings from long-distance suppliers can be lost if a delivery fails to arrive on time or arrives damaged or incomplete as this could cause major delays for a project and add pressure to your budget.

Depending on the build, buying from a local independent business could mean you benefit from local knowledge and expertise.

Think of your carbon footprint when sourcing materials

Waste calculations

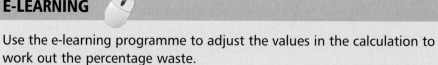

E-LEARNING

Use the e-learning programme to adjust the values in the calculation to work out the percentage waste.

Earlier in this chapter we looked at how to calculate the number of bricks and blocks needed for a project. This was the net amount that is included in a bill of quantities. There is an unavoidable loss of materials due to breakages and wastage cuts, so for this reason a percentage waste is added to the calculation for the actual amount to be ordered. Percentage waste is usually calculated at five to ten per cent of the net amount but you should remember that over ordering can result in increased costs and waste.

To calculate the amount of waste, multiply the original net amount of bricks by the percentage waste figure and then divide this number by one hundred.

For example, if the net amount of bricks required is 340 and you are working with five per cent waste:

To calculate the waste, first multiply the original net amount of bricks by the percentage waste figure.	$340 \times 5 = 1700$
Divide this number by one hundred.	$1700 \div 100 = 17$
Therefore the number of extra bricks needed to allow for wastage is 17. The total number of bricks needed is the original net number of bricks plus the waste.	$340 + 17 = 357$

MATERIALS ORDER FORM			
Order No:		**Date:**	
Site Address:			
Site Name/Address of Supplier:			
Please supply the following order to the above address:			
Description:		**Quantity:**	**Date Required:**
Special Delivery Instructions:			
Signature of Site Manager:			

An example order form

ACTIVITY

How many extra bricks would you need to order for waste if the net amount of bricks is 400 and you are working with five per cent waste?

Show your working out below.

STORAGE OF MATERIALS

Materials should be stored properly for a number of reasons including health and safety, protection against damage, save costs and to ensure efficient use.

Cements and plasters

Must be kept dry and should be stored inside or covered with plastic. They should be stored on pallets off the ground and stacked up to a height of five bags.

Storage for bagged materials

SUSTAINABILITY

Bags of cement and **plaster** must be used on a first-in first-out basis to ensure materials are used by the use-by date to avoid unnecessary waste and should not be left open.

Plaster A white or pinkish mineral formed from heating gypsum at high temperatures. Plaster is used to protect and enhance the appearance of the surface as it provides a joint-less finish.

Aggregates

Must be kept clean and protected from cross contamination, ideally in separate purpose-built bays. They should also be covered and protected from the weather.

Storage for aggregates

Bricks and blocks

Should be stored on a hard level base and protected from frost and water damage. The wrapping should be left on until the bricks or blocks are needed and care should be taken when removing strapping to ensure that nothing is damaged.

Storage for bricks and blocks

HEALTH & SAFETY

All strapping and packaging should be made safe after it has been removed from a pack.

Insulation bats and boards and wall ties

SUSTAINABILITY

Insulation bats and boards should be protected from the weather to avoid deterioration and potential waste.

Bats and boards should be stored flat as twisted boards are difficult to fit and less efficient. Partially built walls where the insulation is still exposed to the weather will need protection.

Storage for insulation

DISPOSAL OF WASTE

SUSTAINABILITY

The UK construction industry produces over 36 million tonnes of landfill waste every year. Sources of waste vary depending on the phase of construction, the method and the type of building, but most waste is produced through over ordering, damage by mishandling, inadequate storage or the weather. Unnecessary packaging of construction materials also contributes a large amount of waste as plastic and cardboard.

Waste minimization strategies

SUSTAINABILITY

There are three basic ways of dealing with waste: Reduce, Reuse, Recycle.

Preventing waste in the first place is the ideal solution and this can be achieved by identifying possible waste streams early on in the build process. It is estimated that over ordering leads to 13 million tonnes of new building materials being wasted every year and improved communication between everyone involved in a build can ensure that exact calculations of required materials are made and that unnecessary waste is prevented. Carefully timed deliveries can help to reduce waste caused by inadequate storage and weather damage.

Once waste has been created, one management solution is for it to be reused, either on the existing or a nearby site. Many materials can be reclaimed and possibly sold to offset the costs of a building project, for example, waste bricks and blocks can be reused as **hardcore**.

Recycling is another option for managing waste. Materials that can be recycled need to be identified early on the build process and separated from the other materials for easy storage, collection and transfer. An effective recycling strategy needs links to established local recycling facilities and contractors.

Hardcore Once the foundation brickwork and blockwork are complete a layer of hardcore, usually formed of broken bricks and gravel bed, is laid on top of the subsoil. Hardcore is the base layer of a solid ground floor. A layer of blinding sand will be laid on top of the hardcore afterwards.

ACTIVITY

Discuss site recycling strategies and research options for recycling unused bricks and blocks.

Make a note of your findings below.

CHECK YOUR KNOWLEDGE

1. **For a 5m² half brick wall including 5 per cent waste, how many bricks do you need to order?**

2. **Which of these are reasons for the correct storage of materials?**

   ☐ a. Health & Safety

   ☐ b. Protection

   ☐ c. Economy

3. **List four ways in which bricks may be classified:**

   1.

   2.

   3.

   4.

4. **Frogs must not exceed what percentage of the volume of the brick?**

   ☐ a. 10 per cent

   ☐ b. 20 per cent

   ☐ c. 30 per cent

5. **What is the ratio for a lime mortar mix?**

   a. __ parts sand

   b. __ parts lime

   c. __ parts cement

Chapter 3

SETTING OUT

LEARNING OBJECTIVES

By the end of this chapter you will be able to:

- Understand the processes involved in **setting out** a building.

- Know about the building and frontage lines.

- Know how to plan and mark out the building shape on the ground.

- Understand excavation and foundation needs.

Setting out The process of marking out a plan on the ground of a site using profile line boards connected by ranging lines.

NOS REFERENCE

Contribute to setting out basic masonry structures

INTRODUCTION

Setting out the building line

The **building line** is usually given as a distance from either the centre of a road, the kerb or an existing building. All building must take place behind this line; you must never build in front of it.

Building line One of the lines set by the local building authority. The building must not be constructed in front of this line.

NOTE ON UK STANDARDS

The building line of a project will have been set by the local authority as part of the planning permission granted to a site.

E-LEARNING

Use the e-learning programme to see an animated explanation of setting out the building line.

Ranging line Heavy duty line that is used for the initial setting out by attaching it to profile boards to mark the trench lines and the face of the walls.

Let's assume our building line has been measured from the rear of the kerb. To set out the building line on the site, you need to measure two square offset lines from the rear of the kerb to the position of the building line. These lines need to be measured at positions that are wider than the proposed building. Place pegs in the ground at the points and fix a **ranging line** between them to set out the building line.

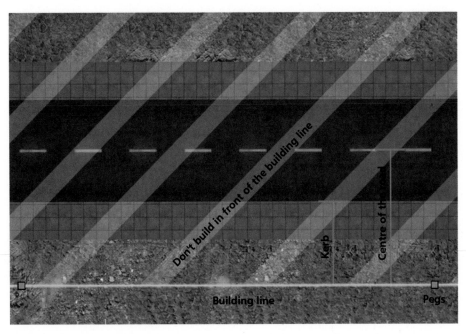

Positioning of the building line

Setting out base lines

E-LEARNING

Use the e-learning programme to see an animated explanation of setting out base lines.

Once the building line has been set out, you can then set out the base or **frontage line** of the building. This may be on the building line itself, just behind it or a set distance away from the kerb.

The first corner peg will be positioned from the dimensions given on the site plan, this will relate to features on the site or a distance from the boundary. Let's assume our frontage line will be on the building line, all we need to do is measure the correct distance from the boundary to locate the first corner of the building. Position peg A at this point. The second peg, B, will then be positioned after measuring the exact width of the building along the frontage line and a ranging line is then fixed between the two pegs.

Frontage line One of the lines attached to the profile boards during the setting out process of a building. The frontage line represents the front wall of the building.

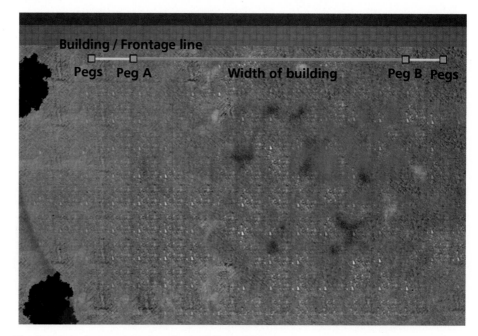

The frontage line and setting the building width

To set the first **right angle line** to the frontage line, attach a line to corner peg B and extend this line the length of the wall being set out. This line must be exactly 90° to the frontage line and is fixed with another peg, C.

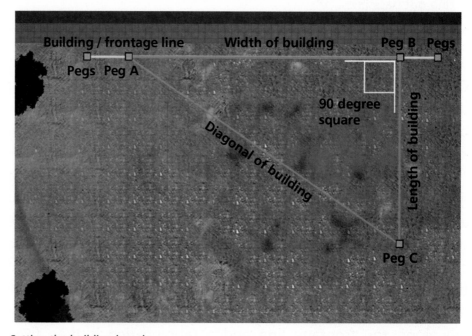

Setting the building length

To check that this line is at 90° you can use the **3:4:5 equation**. For example, if line A to B is 4m and the line B to C is 3m, using the 3:4:5 equation we can work out that line A to C should be 5m.

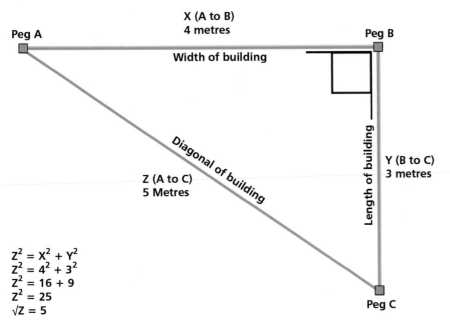

$Z^2 = X^2 + Y^2$
$Z^2 = 4^2 + 3^2$
$Z^2 = 16 + 9$
$Z^2 = 25$
$\sqrt{Z} = 5$

Calulating measurements using 3:4:5 rule

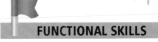

FUNCTIONAL SKILLS

To complete our lines, measure the building length and width from pegs A and C to establish peg D. A final check should be made to ensure the diagonal lines are equal. This can again be done using the 3:4:5 equation.

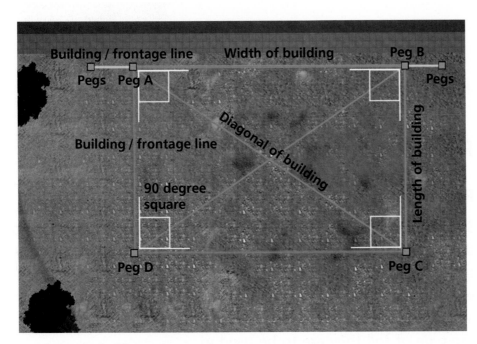

Completing the building measurements

ACTIVITY

Use the 3:4:5 method to work out how long the line A–C will be if the line A–B is 8m and the line B–C is 6m.

Show your working out below.

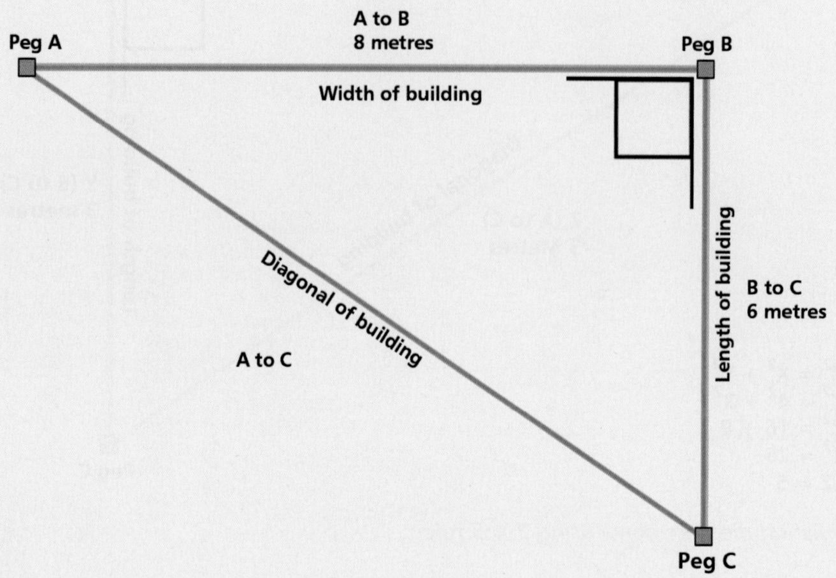

A to B
8 metres
Peg A
Peg B
Width of building
Diagonal of building
A to C
Length of building
B to C
6 metres
Peg C

Profile boards Boards placed at the corners of a building to transfer the plan outline of a building onto the ground. They are held securely in place by square pegs and ranging lines are fixed to them to indicate the foundation, frontage line, right angle lines and back line.

PROFILE BOARDS

Positioning

Single and corner **profile boards** enable the corner points and the position of the walls of a building to be located once the trenches for the foundations have been excavated. They are generally made from a wooden cross board with square pegs attached which can be between 30 and 50mm^2, depending on the type of soil they are to be used in.

Profile boards should be set well away from the planned excavations to allow sufficient working space. This is particularly important if mechanical equipment is needed to carry out the excavation. They should also be set at the same height to maintain the accuracy of setting out.

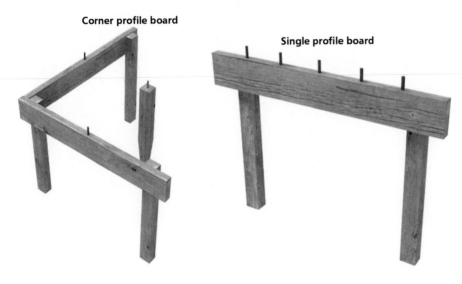

Corner profile board

Single profile board

Profile boards

Ranging lines

The frontage, right angle and **back lines** are transferred to the profile boards by extending the line over the cross board of the profile board and marking the position with a saw cut or a nail. The line is then attached to the cross board at this point with a nail. Once these lines have been transferred the setting out should be checked again.

Back line One of the lines attached to the profile boards during the setting out process of a building. The back line represents the back wall of the building.

ACTIVITY

On the diagram, draw where you think the frontage, right angle and back lines are positioned on the profile boards and label each line.

SETTING UP LINES

Transferring dimensions

E-LEARNING

Use the e-learning programme to see an animated explanation of transferring dimensions.

Load bearing wall A wall which supports the structure of the building above. It should not be removed or altered without professional assistance.

After the profile boards have been set and the base lines marked, the dimensions for the foundations as well as the external and internal **load-bearing walls** are added to the profile boards. It is essential that the profile boards are wide enough to contain all the information required.

ACTIVITY

On the diagram, draw where you think the foundation, external wall and internal wall lines are positioned on the profile boards and label each line.

EXCAVATION

Methods of excavation

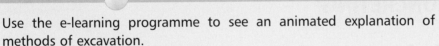

Before the foundation trench is excavated, the line of the trench is transferred from the range lines to the ground using lime or white spray paint. Depending on the excavator's preference either a centre line, or each side of the trench, can be marked.

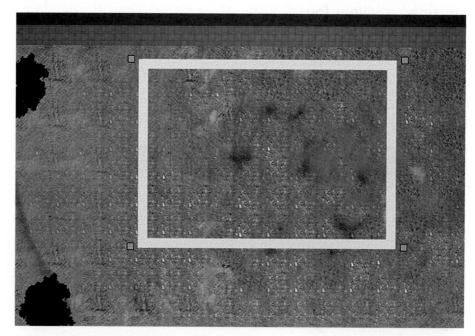

Marking out the foundations

Excavation can then be carried out manually with hand tools or with a mechanical excavator. The method of excavation will depend on a number of factors including:

- amount of soil to be excavated
- type of soil
- access to the site
- time constraints
- safety of the workforce.

CONCRETING

Placing

E-LEARNING

Use the e-learning programme to see an animated explanation of placing concrete.

The decision to use ready mixed concrete or to mix the concrete on site is usually dictated by the size of the foundations and the amount of concrete required.

In small, shallow foundations, the concrete can be mixed on site and placed into the trench using a wheelbarrow where battens are used to guide the concrete into place.

In larger foundations, ready mixed concrete can be poured directly into the trench from the ready mix lorry taking care not to collapse the trench.

Small foundations can be filled manually

Larger foundations can be filled mechanically

Compacting and levelling foundations

After placing the concrete in the foundations you need to remove the trapped air found in the voids of the concrete while it is still in a workable condition. If you don't carry out this step it could lead to:

- The strength of the concrete being reduced.
- Water entering the voids and damaging its reinforcement capabilities.
- Potential visual surface defects such as honeycombing.

To do this you can use a hand tamper to press down and level the concrete. On larger areas it may be possible to use a vibrating poker.

Using a hand tamper

Curing

Concrete is cured by ensuring that when it sets it doesn't lose water too quickly which stops the chemical reaction of hydration. Early drying means the concrete will not reach its maximum strength and durability.

Curing for horizontal surfaces is approximately seven days and during this time, water can be retained in the concrete in a number of ways:

- Covering with **hessian** sheets and spraying them with water to keep them damp.
- Covering with polythene sheets.
- Spraying commercially available curing compounds onto the surface to seal it.

The concrete also needs to be protected from frost and the ideal way to do this is again with hessian sheets but this time the sheets should be as dry as possible.

Curing The method of preventing the loss of water in concrete foundations by slowing the chemical reaction of hydration as the strength of the concrete cannot be maximized if it is dried too quickly. Curing usually takes up to seven days and there are a number of ways concrete can be cured including covering with damp hessian or polythene sheets or spraying the concrete with a curing compound. However, during cold weather, the hessian should be dry to prevent frosting.

Hessian A coarse fabric used to cover the concrete foundations during the curing process.

Curing concrete with hessian sheets

Curing concrete with polythene sheets

Curing concrete by spraying a chemical compound

ACTIVITY

In groups, discuss the advantages and disadvantages of ready mixed concrete versus concrete mixed on site.

List your findings below.

CHECK YOUR KNOWLEDGE

1. **If they are not in the same place, which line should be furthest forward?**

   ☐ a. Building line

   ☐ b. Frontage line

2. **If a building is to be 13.9m wide by 12.4m long, which method of excavation would you select for digging the foundations?**

   ☐ a. Manual

   ☐ b. Mechanical

3. Where should profile boards be set?

☐ a. Inside the planned excavations

☐ b. At the point of the planned excavations

☐ c. Outside the planned excavations

4. What happens if trapped air is not removed from concrete that has been freshly poured into foundation excavations?

☐ a. The concrete won't dry

☐ b. The concrete will be weaker

☐ c. It has no effect at all

5. Which equation rule do you use to check that two lines are at 90° to each other?

☐ a. 2:3:4

☐ b. 3:4:6

☐ c. 3:4:5

Chapter 4

BUILDING BELOW GROUND LEVEL

LEARNING OBJECTIVES

By the end of this chapter you will be able to:

- Understand domestic foundations.

- Know the different types of bonding.

- Know how to build up to the DPC.

- Recognize the different types of flooring used in a building.

NOS REFERENCE

Lay bricks and blocks to line

Contribute to setting out basic masonry structures

Set out masonry structures

Place and finish non-specialist concrete

FOUNDATIONS

Introduction to foundations

E-LEARNING

Use the e-learning programme to see an animated explanation of foundations.

Subsoil The soil immediately below the hardcore of a foundation.

FUNCTIONAL SKILLS

The foundation is the part of the building which is in direct contact with the ground and its purpose is to spread the load from the structure above to an adequate area of the **subsoil** below. It requires strength and stability to prevent undue settlement of a building which can lead to fractures.

The pressures placed on a foundation come from the wall above and the soil below, and are known as compressive forces. As the foundation is made of concrete which is stronger than the subsoil below, the downward force on the foundation from the wall above has to be distributed through a wider area of subsoil. This is usually assumed to be at an angle of 45° from the vertical. Provided that the base of the foundation does not extend beyond this 45° line, the forces remain compressive.

If a wall becomes wider, it follows that the foundation to support it will need to become wider and deeper to keep the base of the foundation within the 45° angle. This would increase the cost of the build significantly with the extra amount of excavation and

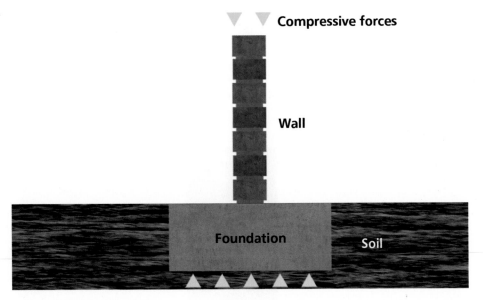

Forces placed on foundations

concrete that would be required, but a shallower foundation would be subject to tensile forces which would cause the foundation to bend. In this case, steel reinforcement is usually used within the concrete to withstand the tensile forces from the wider wall above.

ACTIVITY

On the image shown, draw on the 45° line that shows where the forces on the foundation are distributed.

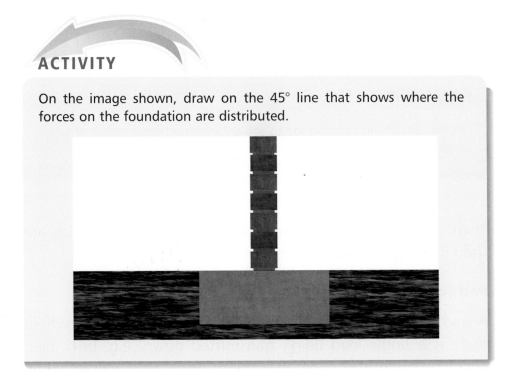

ACTIVITY

On the image shown, draw what you think the foundation should look like.

Types of foundation

E-LEARNING

Use the e-learning programme to see an animated explanation of types of foundation.

Pad foundation A type of foundation where a block of concrete is used when there is a single load being transmitted down a brick pier, concrete column or steel stanchion. Predominantly used in commercial buildings, not domestic low level structures.

There are a number of different types of foundation which are used in different circumstances.

Pad foundation

A **pad foundation** is a block of concrete which is used where there is a single load being transmitted down, e.g. brick pier, concrete column or steel stanchion. They are predominantly used in commercial buildings not domestic low level structures.

Pad foundation

Strip foundation

Strip foundations are generally used for low to medium rise domestic and industrial buildings. They are made from a continuous concrete mass situated under the wall, which must be a minimum of 150mm thick with an equal projection each side of the wall of at least the same measurement.

> **Strip foundation** A common type of foundation generally used for low to medium rise domestic and industrial buildings. It is made from a continuous concrete mass situated under the wall which must be a minimum of 150mm thick, with an equal projection each side of the wall of at least the same measurement.

Strip foundation

Wide strip foundation

Where a traditional strip foundation is unsuitable due to the subsoil, a **wide strip foundation** is used. As we have already said, as the foundation gets wider it must also become deeper to avoid tensile stress. Where this is uneconomical, reinforcement is used.

> **Wide strip foundation** When strip foundation is unsuitable due to the subsoil a wide strip foundation is used. As the foundation gets wider it must also become deeper to avoid tensile stress. Where this is uneconomical, reinforcement is used.

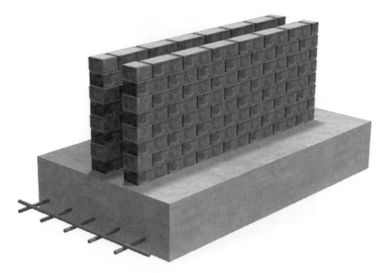

Wide strip foundation

Step strip foundation

Step strip foundations (see **step foundation**) are used on sloping sites where they reduce the amount of excavation needed and avoid different settlement rates in different layers of the subsoil. Construction begins at the lowest point and the foundations overlap as they move up the slope. The overlap must be twice as thick as the step or foundation thickness, whichever is the largest.

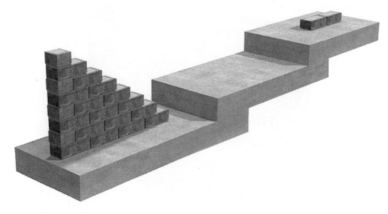

Step foundation

Narrow strip foundation

Narrow strip or trench fill foundations are used where the amount of space required to build on top of the concrete strip would make the foundation wider than it needed to be for structural reasons. A narrow trench is excavated, filled with concrete and the bricklayer then begins to build from ground level rather than from within the trench itself.

Narrow strip foundation

BONDING

Terminology

It is useful to know some of the terminology used in brickwork. Some commonly used terms are:

Bond

There are two types of bonds, half lap and quarter lap. This refers to how much one course of bricks overlaps another course. Bonds have many different arrangements and are used for structural and decorative purposes.

Quarter lap bond

Brickwork A solid wall built of bricks, laid to bond and in mortar. Used to be the most common load-bearing external wall construction. Mainly finished with fair faced bricks and pointed or rendered. Minimal maintenance required but as properties age partial or complete re-pointing or re-rendering respectively may become necessary.

Bond The arrangement of bricks to prevent vertical joints in succeeding course to coincide. This increases the stability and load-bearing capacity of the wall. The most common bonds in bricklaying are: English, Flemish and Stretcher bonds. The type of bond used may be chosen for strength, cost or decorative appearance.

Half lap bond

Bat

Bats are a cut brick, for example, a quarter, half or three quarter bat.

Bat Part of a brick when cut square across its width. Bats cut as a quarter, half, or three quarters of the brick length are used to achieve a variety of bonding arrangements. A cut brick is any other length, cut from the whole brick, which is used to fit required wall dimensions.

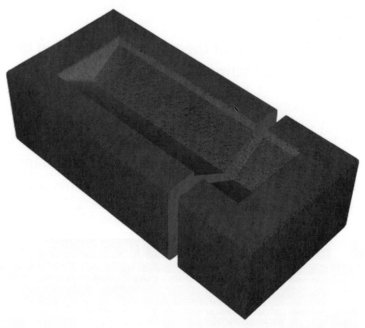

Quarter bat

Half bat

Three quarter bat

Quoin

A **quoin** is the external angle on the outside corner of a building.

> **Quoin** The external angle of a building at a corner of the building.

Closer brick A brick cut lengthways to give a reduced width. Used where the appearance of a full brick is required but the depth of the brickwork will not accommodate a full width, such as where a pier is inserted into a wall. There are a number of types of closer bricks including king closer, queen closer, bevelled closer and mitred closer.

King closer A type of closer brick with a bevel cut with a diagonal cut at one header face.

Queen closer A type of closer brick with a cut on the centre line along its length to produce a 56mm closer. This type of brick is used in all quarter bonds to set the required lap and must be placed immediately after the quoin header and in no other position.

Bevelled closer A type of closer brick with a bevel along its length reducing a header at one end to 56mm.

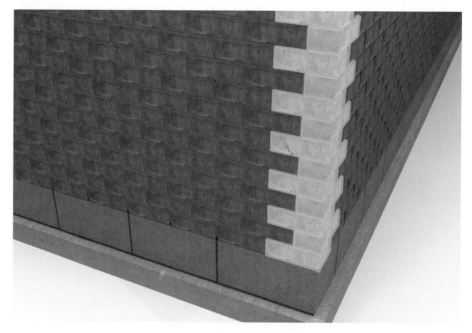

Quoin of a wall

Closer

Closer bricks come in a number of different formats. There are **king closers**, **queen closers**, **bevelled closers** (*closures*) and mitred closers. These bricks are cut lengthways at different angles and are used when a modification to the bond is required.

King closer

Queen closer

Bevelled closer

ACTIVITY

FUNCTIONAL SKILLS

If a brick is 215mm in length, what are the measurements for quarter, half and three quarter bats?

Quarter bat: _____mm

Half bat: _____mm

Three quarter bat: _____mm

Bond arrangements

Bonds can be half lap or quarter lap and can be done in a number of arrangements that serve structural as well as decorative purposes.

ACTIVITY

Here are some of the most common bond arrangements. Can you match the correct bond type to the description and image?

English bond	A half lap bond arrangement which is a very simple bond where all the bricks are laid as stretchers and a half bat is used on alternate courses to maintain the bond. This bond is only suitable for half brick walls which are not stable enough to stand by themselves. They are usually built as part of a cavity wall and tied together with wall ties or attached to the timber frame of a building.	
Flemish bond	A quarter lap bond arrangement which is very strong and is generally used where strength is a higher priority than appearance. It is built by laying alternate header and stretcher courses in the wall and the bond is maintained by laying a queen closer next to the quoin header.	
Stretcher bond	A quarter lap arrangement which is considered to be the most decorative bond where stretchers and headers are alternated in the same course. It is maintained by laying a closer next to the quoin header.	

BRICKWORK TO DPC

Setting out corners

After laying the concrete in the foundation trenches and before building can begin, the positions of the corners of the building need to be marked.

Using the profile boards marked at the setting out stage, ranging lines are attached to show where the quoins or outside corners of the building should be. A **spirit level** is then used to transfer these positions down onto the concrete. A thin layer of **mortar** is laid on the concrete foundation and lines cut into it with a trowel to mark the position of the corners.

Spirit level A tool used to check true vertical and horizontal lines indicated by a bubble in spirit-filled vials.

Mortar A mixture of sand, cement (sometimes with lime and/or additives) and water, used to bond stones and bricks. Can be mixed by hand or mechanically on or off site.

Marking corner positions

Erecting corners

E-LEARNING

Use the e-learning programme to see an animated explanation of erecting corners.

Datum peg Square timber peg used to mark the height of the brickwork up to damp proof course (DPC) level.

As part of the setting out process, a **datum peg** would have been used to indicate a level in the building, usually the **damp proof course**. The distance from the concrete foundation up to this level should be equal to a number of brick courses to avoid wastage.

To start building, the corner of the wall is first dry bonded or laid without mortar to establish the bond and ensure there are no breaks.

Damp proof course (DPC) A horizontal layer of impervious materials such as bituminous felt, asphalt, two courses of slate or two courses of **engineering bricks**. It is usually laid at 150mm above ground level to prevent moisture rising. For walls subject to high compressive loads. It is also necessary to form an impervious barrier in cavity walls when bridging openings (e.g. doors and windows). Damp proof course is commonly known as DPC.

Dry bonding bricks

Engineering brick A strong and dense type of brick, impervious to water so ideal for use in damp areas.

To begin building the corners, the first course of bricks is laid on a mortar bed directly onto the concrete foundation. Care must be taken to ensure these bricks are straight and either line up against the scored line marked with the trowel on the foundation, or in this case, the foundation block.

Each course of bricks should be reduced by one brick; this is known as raking back. Build until the level of the datum peg is reached. Using your spirit level, always make sure your bricks are level and plumb.

Forming corners

Erecting walls

Once the corners have been built, a string line should be attached to each corner using corner blocks to keep the brickwork straight. Lay one course of bricks from corner to corner before moving on to the next course and always keep the corners higher than the rest of the brickwork.

Laying courses of bricks

First, lay a bed of mortar along the existing course of brickwork then use the point of your trowel along the centre of the spread to push the mortar to the front of the bricks.

When laying a brick, butter up the header face of the brick with some mortar using your trowel to smooth, then place the buttered edge of the brick against the adjoining brick making sure the brick is level and adjacent to your string line. Tap the brick with the trowel to make any adjustments. Mortar joints should be approximately 10mm thick.

As the brickwork progresses, use the string line, spirit level and gauging rod to make sure the course of bricks is level and plumb.

ACTIVITY

On the diagrams shown, draw how you would position the spirit level to test the bricks are level and plumb, and the gauge rod to test the gauge of the bricks.

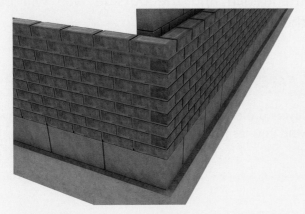

Testing level

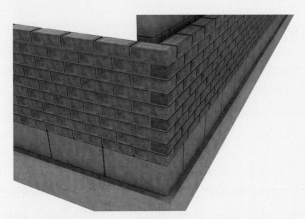

Testing plumb

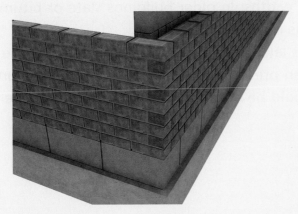

Checking gauge

Working below ground

When working below ground up to the level of the datum peg, materials need to be set out above ground without placing undue pressure on the sides of the trench. Space may be very limited in the trench and the outside wall will be easier to build than the inside.

HEALTH & SAFETY

Some bricklayers prefer to work at ground level and lean down into the trench to avoid injuries from the stones that may protrude into the side of the trench.

Damp proof course (DPC)

E-LEARNING

Use the e-learning programme to see an animated explanation of damp proof course.

Once the brickwork has reached the level of the datum peg, the damp proof course or DPC is laid. The DPC is a barrier to prevent the movement of water. It is usually made from pitch polymer, polythene or polyethylene and is supplied in rolls of varying lengths and widths. In older buildings slate or bitumen felt was used but this is now in decline.

The DPC is laid on a mortar bed beginning at one end of the wall and then pressed into the mortar bed as it is unrolled. Any overlaps should be of equal size to the width of the DPC.

DPC laid over brickwork

DPC being rolled out

Overlapping the DPC

Positioning DPCs

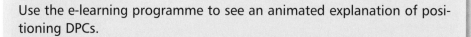

E-LEARNING

Use the e-learning programme to see an animated explanation of positioning DPCs.

The DPC should be positioned a minimum of 150mm above ground level and should be flush with or slightly over the external face of the wall. Never cover the edge of the DPC with mortar and make sure the DPC does not protrude into the cavity where mortar can collect.

A DPC should also be placed at the base of internal walls that are built on foundations. Vertical DPCs around windows and doors should project a minimum of 25mm beyond the closer position and be touching the window or door frame.

NOTE ON UK STANDARDS

Current building regulations give specific advice as to how and where DPCs should be positioned.

Positioning the DPC

TYPES OF FLOORING

Solid ground floors

E-LEARNING

Use the e-learning programme to see an animated explanation of solid ground floors.

Once the foundation brickwork is complete, the ground floors of the building can be completed.

Solid ground floors consist of layers of material, starting with a thick layer of well compacted hardcore.

Next is a layer of compacted sand known as **blinding** followed by the **damp proof membrane (DPM)** which is overlapped into the DPC of the brickwork to form a continuous layer.

NOTE ON UK STANDARDS

Building regulations require all ground floors to be insulated against heat loss and this is the next layer. Insulation can consist of a number of materials including expanded polystyrene and rigid foam.

Oversite concrete is layered on top of the insulation and should be a minimum of 100mm thick. It is not necessary to trowel finish this layer as any **floor screed** used later will adhere better to a tamped surface. The final layer would be the floor screed which is laid later in the project.

Blinding A layer of compacted sand on top of a hardcore bed before the damp proof membrane (DPM) is laid.

Damp proof membrane (DPM) A layer of plastic sheeting laid over the blinding sand above a hardcore of a modern building, to prevent moisture rising from the ground into the floor structure. For this layer to become fully effective, it should be connected to the damp proof course (DPC) in the surrounding walls. Damp proof membrane is commonly known as DPM.

Oversite concrete A layer of concrete which is at least 100mm thick that is laid over the insulation in a solid ground floor. It is not necessary to trowel-finish this concrete as the floor screed to be laid will adhere better to a tamped surface.

Floor screed The final layer of concrete laid on top of the oversite concrete to level off. The floor screed is usually laid later on in the project.

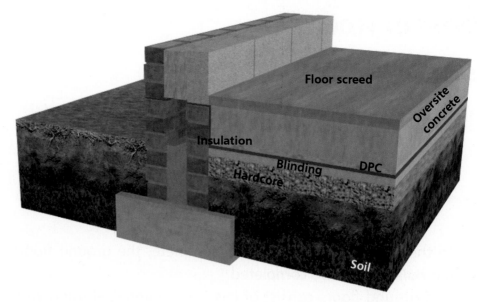

Layers of a solid ground floor

ACTIVITY

When materials are drawn on diagrams they usually have a specific pattern. Use the internet to find out the patterns for the following materials and draw them in the boxes shown.

Soil	Hardcore	Blinding
Insulation	Oversite Concrete	Floor screed

Hollow ground floors

Block and beam is the most common method of creating a hollow ground floor, although suspended timber floors and timber **joists** can also be used. The block and beam method has a number of performance benefits including acoustic, fire resistance and insulation. As it is not affected by damp it is not prone to rot or vermin. Block and beam floors are fairly straightforward to install. They use inverted T beams to span the floor area making sure they are supported across larger floor areas. The beams are then filled in with either lightweight aircrete or aggregate blocks. Another option is specialist expanded polystyrene blocks which provide high levels of thermal insulation and are a **sustainable** and efficient alternative. Once the block and beam suspended floor has been laid it can be finished off with the floor screed.

Joist A beam that supports a ceiling or floor.

Sustainable Materials that have been sourced by causing little or no damage to the environment.

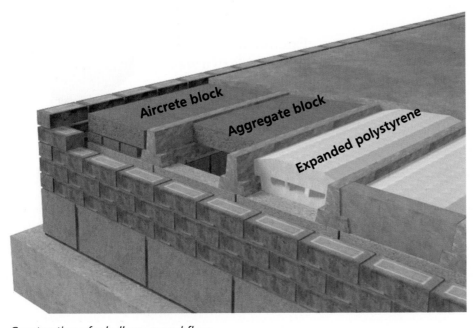

Construction of a hollow ground floor

CHECK YOUR KNOWLEDGE

1. **At what angle is the compressive force from the wall above transmitted through the foundation to the subsoil?**

   ☐ a. 35°

   ☐ b. 45°

   ☐ c. 55°

2. **Which brick term matches each description?**

Brick term	Description	Figure
Type of bond	Patterns of brick-work used for structural and decorative purposes.	
Bat	Bricks cut width-ways, available in quarters, halves or three quarters.	
Quoin	External angle on the outside of a wall at the corner of a building.	
Closer	Bricks cut length-ways at different angles, available in king, queen, bevelled and mitred.	

3. **What is the recommended minimum thickness of the layer of oversite concrete in a solid ground floor?**

☐ a. 300mm

☐ b. 200mm

☐ c. 100mm

4. **List three different types of foundation:**

1.

2.

3.

5. **How far above ground level should the DPC be positioned?**

☐ a. 150mm

☐ b. 200mm

☐ c. 250mm

Chapter 5

BUILDING ABOVE GROUND LEVEL

LEARNING OBJECTIVES

By the end of this chapter you will be able to:

- Know why dry bonding is important.

- Explain the make up of a cavity wall and why it is used.

- List the different types of jointing and why they are used.

- Know how and why openings are bridged.

- List the different types of internal wall.

- Understand how joist hangers and gable ends are created.

- Know what checks should be carried out once work is complete.

Dry bonding A brick or timber joint that is not bonded with mortar or adhesive.

Jointing The process of finishing off mortar joints in brickwork or blockwork to waterproof the wall. Timing is crucial for jointing as the mortar may crumble if jointing is carried out after the mortar has dried.

Joist hanger Metal slots installed to wall plates, rafters or existing joists to support a row of joists. Available in different sizes to accommodate different joists.

Gable The triangular upper part of a wall at the end of a ridged roof.

Broken bond This occurs when brick sizes will not fit the designed wall length. This is a common situation and requires careful planning (i.e. dry bonding) for quality face work. Where there is a broken bond and bricks need to be cut, the cut bricks should be placed under window and door openings to minimize the number of courses with cut bricks, leaving the majority of the wall true to bond.

NOS REFERENCE

Lay bricks and blocks to line

Joint brick and block structures

Erect masonry structures

Erect thin joint masonry structures

Repair and maintain masonry structures

Develop and maintain good working relationships

DRY BONDING

Setting out the bond

E-LEARNING

Use the e-learning programme for an animated explanation of setting out the bond.

Setting out the bond or dry bonding of brickwork is designed to create a matching and balanced appearance of bricks and to avoid wasteful cutting. In an ideal world, walls and the size and position of openings would be designed around the size of brick being used.

The usual practice is to dry bond the bricks from one end of the wall, placing any necessary **broken bond** or cut brick under a door or window opening. This avoids breaking the bond and doing any unnecessary cutting, and leaves symmetrical bonding at each side of any **reveals** or openings in the brickwork. In practice this rarely happens and the solution lies in the skill of the bricklayer.

A **reverse bond** is an alternative to a broken bond. When the dimensions of a wall require cut bricks, the use of reverse bonds can be neater and more cost effective.

Dry bond to plan openings

Reveal The sides of door and window openings which should be identified when setting out the first and second course of bricks. This is to ensure that there are no unbroken perpends throughout the height of the wall.

Reverse bond An alternative to a broken bond. This bond is achieved by a stretcher brick at one end with a header at the other end on the same course.

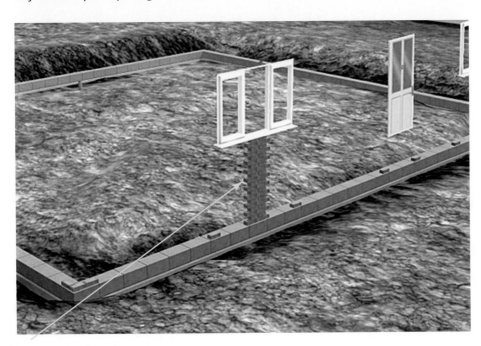

Place cuts under openings

Perpends and reveals

Perpends are the position of the vertical joints in brickwork. It is essential that they continue vertically from the first course of bricks to the top of the brickwork, and should be checked with a spirit level every four or five courses to make sure they are plumb.

Perpends The position of the vertical joints in brickwork. It is essential that they continue vertically from the first course of bricks to the top of the brickwork and should be checked with a spirit level every four or five courses to make sure they are plumb.

Reveals are the sides of door and window openings which should be identified when setting out the first and second course of bricks. This is to ensure that there are no unbroken perpends throughout the height of the wall.

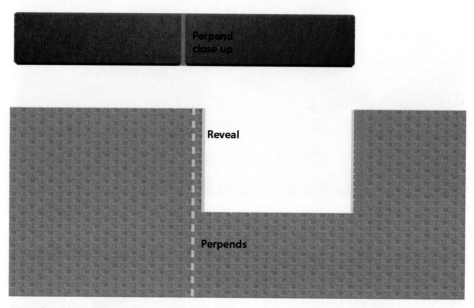

Perpends and reveals

CAVITY WALLS

Introduction to cavity walls

Cavity walls are a means of preventing damp inside domestic buildings. The two walls are referred to as the inner and **outer leaf** and the space between them is known as the cavity. Wall ties are used to tie the inner and outer leaf of the wall together.

Outer leaf The external wall of a cavity construction. The outer leaf wall is tied to the inner leaf using wall ties.

NOTE ON UK STANDARDS

This cavity must be a minimum of 50mm wide but is usually wider to allow for sufficient insulation material to meet current building regulations.

ACTIVITY

Label the image shown here with what you think is the inner wall, the outer wall and the cavity.

Cavity wall construction below ground

Cavity walls below ground can be constructed using the following methods.

Cavity wall of two walls of solid blocks

Cavity walls below ground can be built from solid foundation blocks which are strong and dense. The space below ground has a **cavity fill** applied to it. This is a lean concrete mix used to prevent water filling the cavity and to resist the lateral pressures being applied. **Weep holes** are added at 900mm centres above the concrete mix to allow any water to escape. **Blockwork** should finish and facework begin at least one course of bricks below ground level to prevent uneven ground exposing the blockwork and the DPC should be a minimum of 150mm above ground level.

Cavity fill Lean mix concrete filling of cavity from top of foundations to ground level. Provided to make wall below ground level solid and withstand the lateral pressure exerted by the subsoil on either side of the wall and prevent wall caving in. This concrete must be kept 150mm below the horizontal damp proof course (DPC) to allow the cavity to extend below it.

Weep holes In some parts of an external wall, water can collect behind the internal face within the cavity tray above window and door openings. Draining of this water can be achieved by opening cross joints spaced at regular intervals and installing plastic ducts or vents to keep insects out of the cavity.

Blockwork Walls built of blocks as opposed to bricks, which may be used externally with a rendered finish, but more widely for the internal walls of cavity walls.

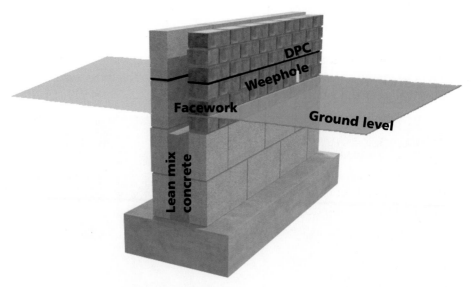

Cavity wall of two walls of solid blocks

Cavity wall on solid foundation blocks

Cavity walls can also be built on solid foundation blocks that are the width of the cavity wall above. Facework should begin at least one course of bricks below ground level to prevent uneven ground exposing the blocks where the cavity begins. In this case, the cavity does not need infilling with concrete.

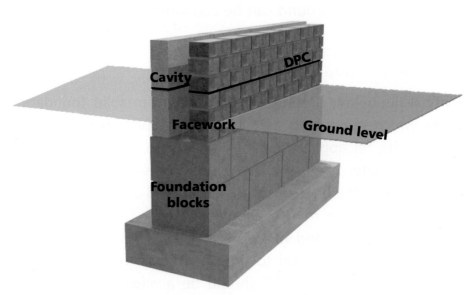

Cavity wall on solid foundation blocks

Cavity wall construction above ground

As the cavity wall is constructed, wall ties are used to tie the two walls together.

NOTE ON UK STANDARDS

The types of wall tie will have been specified by the architect and the position should be in accordance with building regulations or the masonry code of practice.

Wall ties should be placed correctly to prevent damp penetrating the inner leaf, and cavity battens may be used to prevent mortar droppings falling into the cavity.

Insulation material is added to the cavity as the wall is being built unless it is to be injected afterwards. Full fill flexible insulation bats fit between rows of wall ties, or where necessary, small cuts can be made in the bat to allow it to fit over wall ties.

Partial fill rigid cavity boards use special wall ties to fix them to the face of the inner leaf of the cavity.

Placing cavity battens

JOINTING AND POINTING

Jointing

Jointing is the process of finishing off mortar joints in brickwork or blockwork to waterproof the wall and give it an aesthetic value. It is also forms an important part of the facework of the wall and well-formed joints and clean brickwork are the mark of a professional bricklayer. Timing is crucial when jointing. If the mortar is still too wet, the joint will not be crisp and the mortar may be removed from the joint. If the mortar is left too long, particularly when the weather is hot, it will be too dry and jointing may cause the surface of the mortar to crumble.

Finishing off a joint

Types of joints

There are a number of different types of joint. These will be specified by the architect and may be chosen to match the existing joints when working on an extension or renovation project.

Flush

Flush joints are created by cleaning off excess mortar close to the surface of the brickwork and then later, sometimes even the next day, brushing the surface of the mortar with a light bristle brush. This type of jointing requires experience, care and attention to detail.

Half-round tooled

Half-round tooled joints are created by running a jointer along the joints to achieve the desired effect. Perp joints should always be completed first.

Jointer A tool used in bricklaying for achieving a half-round tooled mortar joint.

Raked or square recessed

Raked or square recessed joints are where the surface of the mortar sits flat at a specified depth below the surface of the brick. A chariot or improvised depth gauge is used to remove the mortar and the surface is polished once the mortar is completely dry. This type of joint does not repel water and cannot be used if the wall is in an exposed area.

Chariot Tool used in bricklaying for achieving a raked or squared recessed mortar joint.

Weatherstruck

Weatherstruck joints are designed to let the water run off the surface of the joint. They are created using a pointing trowel and the excess mortar produced at the base of each joint is then removed using a tool called a Frenchman.

Pointing trowel A trowel used in bricklaying for achieving a weatherstruck mortar joint.

Frenchman A tool made by craftsmen, usually from an old table knife. The end of the knife blade is used for weatherstruck joints by cutting surplus mortar from bed and cross joints.

ACTIVITY

On the images shown, draw how you think each joint would look.

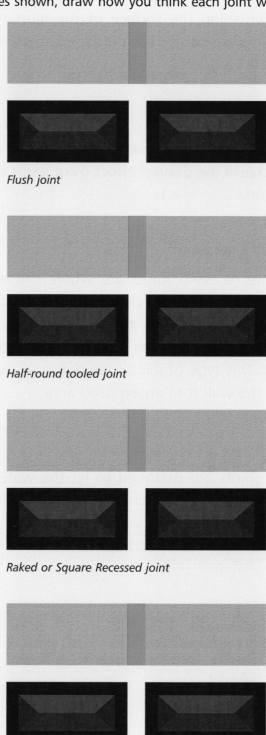

Flush joint

Half-round tooled joint

Raked or Square Recessed joint

Weatherstruck joint

Pointing

E-LEARNING

Use the e-learning programme for an animated explanation of pointing.

Pointing is the process of finishing off joints that have been raked out to a depth of between 15 and 20mm. Joints may be raked out on new builds where the mortar is to be a different colour to contrast with the brickwork or on renovation projects where the existing mortar has deteriorated. In either case, a dry brush should be used to remove all loose material before pointing begins.

When pointing, the perp joints are filled in first and the mortar is compacted with the inset on the left and the cut on the right so that every joint looks the same. The mortar should be fatty and if the surface is damped down first, the amount of water being removed from the mortar as it dries will be reduced, ensuring the mortar does not dry weak and crumbly.

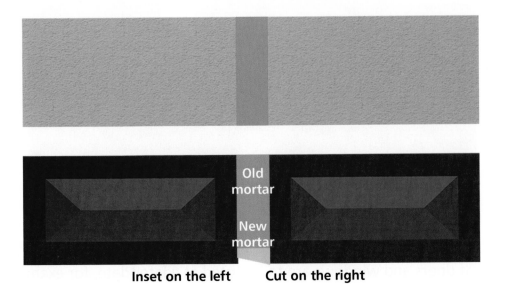

	Old mortar	
	New mortar	
Inset on the left		**Cut on the right**

Pointing brickwork

BRIDGING OPENINGS

Doors and windows

Door and window openings are created while a cavity wall is being constructed. The door or window frame can either be built into the wall as the wall is constructed or pre-determined-sized openings can be left in the wall for doors and windows to be fitted at a later date.

Pre-constructed door and window frames are generally made of timber or metal and are secured into the brickwork with ties which are built into horizontal joints as the brickwork progresses. Timber or scaffold boards then hold the frame in position until the mortar dries.

Fixing frames to the brickwork

uPVC A type of stable plastic used in the manufacture of double-glazed window frames, doors and cladding.

Dummy frame A timber frame used whilst the wall is being built to temporarily indicate where openings (e.g. doors and windows) will be. The frame is slightly larger than the door or window to be fitted.

If doors and windows are to be fitted at a later date, for example **uPVC** doors and windows, an opening needs to be created in the brickwork. This is achieved using a **dummy frame** called a profile which is usually slightly larger than the door or window to be fitted.

Using profiles to create openings

Cills and thresholds

At the base of a window frame is a cill and at the base of a door frame is a **door threshold**. Both are designed to ensure water runs away from the building and not towards it.

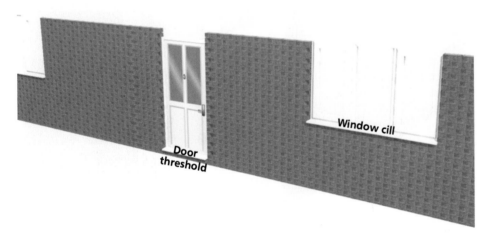

Window cill and door threshold

To create a **window cill**, a **cavity closer** is used to seal the cavity wall. The indoor window board is placed on top of the cavity and the outdoor window cill is placed on the outer leaf of the cavity wall.

Door threshold The board at the base of an external door, designed to ensure water runs away from the building.

Window cill The board at the external base of a window designed to ensure water runs away from the building.

Cavity closer An insulated plastic extrusion used to close off openings (e.g. windows and doors).

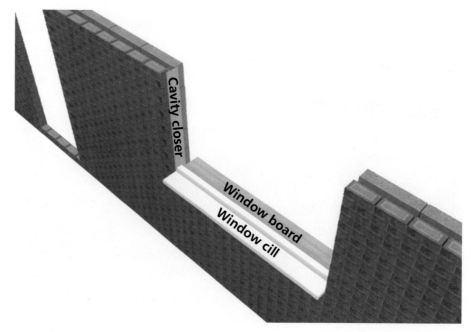

Type of window cill construction

A door frame usually has a threshold at the base but if it hasn't, a concrete or brick-on-edge threshold will need to be created. In both cases, a water bar is used to prevent ingress of water.

Type of door threshold construction

Lintels

E-LEARNING

Use the e-learning programme for an animated explanation of lintels.

Lintels are inserted into a wall to support an opening and are usually made from steel or concrete. In some cases however, they can be made from plastic, stone or brick. They can also contain insulation material. A lintel is exposed to compressive forces from above and tensile forces from below which can cause them to bend and even fail if the correct material is not used.

> **Lintel** A horizontal beam of timber (old buildings), stone, concrete or steel (new buildings), spanning the openings (e.g. doors and windows) in a wall to support the structure above.

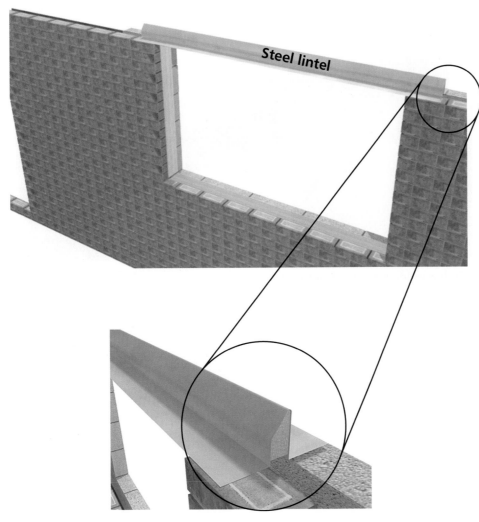

Steel lintel

Steel lintel with insulation

DPC trays

> **DPC tray** A membrane located above openings (e.g. windows and doors). Any water that penetrates through the openings is drained down the DPC tray and expelled from the wall through weep holes.

Openings in the brickwork need to be protected with a **DPC tray**, this is usually in the form of a membrane. On some occasions a rigid DPC tray with stop ends may be required.

Any water that penetrates the outer wall above the opening will drain down the inside of the wall to the DPC tray. From here it is expelled from the wall through weep holes in the outer leaf.

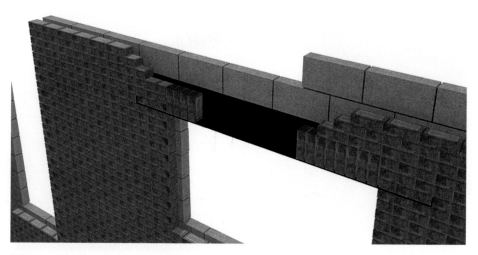

DPC tray over a window opening

ACTIVITY

In the space below, draw a side profile diagram of how the DPC tray would be positioned over a steel lintel.

INTERNAL WALLS

Block internal walls

Where an internal or partition wall is to be constructed, blocks are the most common material used. They have excellent sound proofing and insulation qualities and also provide secure fixing for radiators and other household fixtures. An internal solid wall would usually be a load bearing wall whereas an internal cavity wall is more likely to be a partition wall between buildings.

Solid internal wall

Cavity internal wall

JOIST HANGERS AND GABLE ENDS

Joist hangers

Joist hangers come in different sizes and types and can be used to support a row of joists. They are fixed to the top edge of an existing joist, rafter or **wall plate**.

> **Wall plate** A horizontal timber bedded in mortar on top of the wall. This provides the support ceiling joists, rafters and roof truss.

Timber to masonry joist hangers

Timber to timber joist hangers

Constructing a gable end

Roof truss The timber frame structure of a roof, usually factory made and delivered to site.

The gable end of a wall is constructed once the wall has reached the height of the wall plate and the roof trusses have been finished. Timber battens are added to the roof truss and lines attached to show the shape of the gable end. A string line is lowered from the top batten to maintain the plumb of the gable.

As the bricklayer builds the gable end, he cuts the bricks to the shape of the string line using a raking cut. The bricks can be cut with a hammer and bolster or alternatively using a motorized cutting machine.

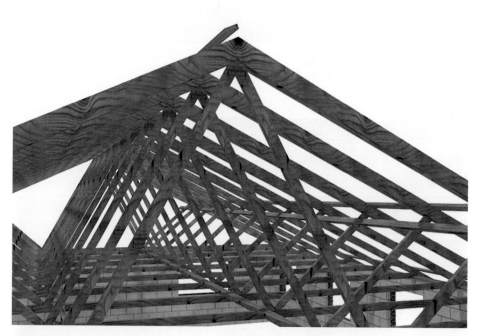

Constructing a gable end

CHECKS

Checks to be carried out

E-LEARNING

Use the e-learning programme to read the checks to be carried out in a flip-book format.

There are a number of checks that should be carried out throughout any bricklaying.

Gauge	A **gauge rod** is a piece of timber marked to show the spacing between one brick plus the associated joint. It is used to ensure that each course of bricks is the correct height at the corners of the wall.
Level	The corner bricks are set to the correct height and a spirit level is used to ensure that each course of bricks matches this level.
Plumb	The wall face needs to be vertical or 'plumb'. This is checked with a spirit level on one side of the wall at regular intervals.
Straight	Once a wall is plumb, a spirit level is used to ensure the wall is straight (ranged). Again this is only checked on one side of the wall.

Gauge rod A timber batten long enough to reach one storey high, marked with the top of each course of bricks.

Customer care

Whether you are working on a large construction site or a renovation for a private client, there are a number of customer care concerns that should be taken into consideration.

HEALTH & SAFETY

- Access to the site should be maintained at all times.
- The site should be kept clean and free from debris and rubbish.
- Health and safety should be of the utmost priority.
- You should be polite and helpful to all customers and people working on site.
- Ensure that you always keep the customer informed.
- Always be on time and professional.
- The job should be completed on time and to a high standard.

CHECK YOUR KNOWLEDGE

1. Why is dry bonding important?

☐ a. It creates a balanced appearance of brickwork

☐ b. It helps to calculate the number of bricks needed for a project

☐ c. It avoids broken perpends throughout the height of the wall

2. Match the name of these joint finishes with the images shown.

Flush	
Half-round tooled	

| Raked or square recessed | 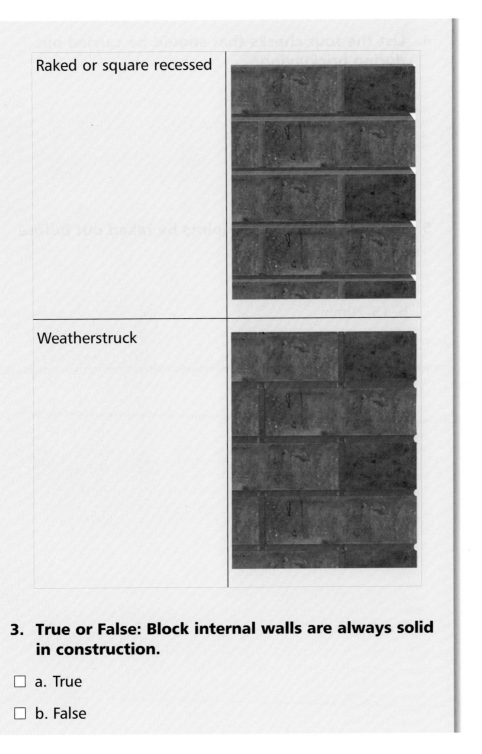 |
| Weatherstruck | |

3. True or False: Block internal walls are always solid in construction.

☐ a. True

☐ b. False

4. **List the four checks that should be carried out during bricklaying.**

   1.

   2.

   3.

   4.

5. **To what depth should joints be raked out before repointing?**

   ☐ a. 10–15mm

   ☐ b. 15–20mm

   ☐ c. 20–25mm

Chapter 6

END TEST

END TEST OBJECTIVES

The end test will check your knowledge on the information held within this workbook.

THE TEST

E-LEARNING

Use the e-learning programme to complete this test online.

1. **What checks are likely to have been carried out on a site prior to the start of brickwork?**

   ☐ a. Study of council records

   ☐ b. Evidence of previous use of the site

   ☐ c. The distance to local services

   ☐ d. Study of the contours of the site

2. **What would the actual measurement be for a line of 100mm on a drawing in 1:20 scale?**

3. **What is the usual percentage waste amount added to the net amount of bricks or blocks?**

   ☐ a. 15–20 per cent

   ☐ b. 10–15 per cent

   ☐ c. 5–10 per cent

4. **For a 102.5mm wide wall (½ brick thick) which is 3m² in area with 5 per cent waste, how many bricks would you order?**

5. **Approximately how many million tonnes of waste does the UK construction industry send to landfill each year?**

   ☐ a. 26

   ☐ b. 36

   ☐ c. 46

6. **Who sets the position of the building line?**

   ☐ a. Architect

   ☐ b. Bricklayer

   ☐ c. Local authority

7. **Approximately how long is the curing process for a horizontal surface of concrete?**

   ☐ a. 7 hours

   ☐ b. 7 days

   ☐ c. 7 weeks

8. **At what angle are the forces spread through the foundation to evenly distribute the loads from the vertical angle of the wall?**

   ☐ a. 30°

   ☐ b. 45°

   ☐ c. 60°

9. Label the different layers of a solid ground floor.

10. The usual practice when dry bonding is to start at the centre of the wall.

☐ a. True

☐ b. False

11. What are perpends?

☐ a. The joint at the corner of a brick

☐ b. The hollow in a brick

☐ c. The vertical joints in brickwork

12. Label each part of the cavity wall shown.

13. The cavity in a wall should be at least 50mm.

☐ a. True

☐ b. False

14. What is the correct position for a wall tie?

☐ a. Sloping towards the inside wall

☐ b. Sloping towards the outside wall

15. To which leaf of a cavity wall is partial fill insulation fixed?

☐ a. Outer leaf

☐ b. Inner leaf

16. Pointing is only carried out on old buildings.

☐ a. True

☐ b. False

17. If a window or door is to be fitted after brickwork is complete, what is the name of the frame used to size the opening?

☐ a. Prefit

☐ b. Profile

☐ c. Perpend

18. A lintel is subjected to which forces?

☐ a. Compressive

☐ b. Tensile

☐ c. Both

19. When is the gable end of a house constructed?

☐ a. When the brickwork reaches the wall plate but before the roof trusses are added

☐ b. When the brickwork reaches the wall plate and after the roof trusses are finished

☐ c. When the brickwork reaches the wall plate and the roof trusses and roof tiling have been completed

20. Which checks should be carried out during bricklaying

☐ a. Angle

☐ b. Gauge

☐ c. Level

☐ d. Line

☐ e. Plumb

☐ f. Straight

Answers to Check Your Knowledge and End Test

CHAPTER 1

1. **False: It is the responsibility of the architect to carry out a full site analysis before you start any bricklaying.**

2. **False: Planning permission is not always required. Check the planning portal website for more information.**

3. **False: Bricklayers can work for a number of employers including private households, building contractors, local authorities or specialist contractors.**

4. **A: In a drawing to a scale of 1:10, 100mm will represent 1000mm or 1m.**

5. **C: The Construction Design and Management Regulations were updated in 2007.**

CHAPTER 2

1. **The amount of bricks to order for a 5m² half brick wall including a 5 per cent waste is 315.**

   We need 60 bricks per m² of wall = 5 × 60 = 300

To calculate 5 per cent waste = 300 × 0.05 (or 5 per cent) = 15

   Total bricks = 300 + 15 = 315

2. **A, B, C: All of these are reasons to store materials correctly.**

3. **Bricks can be classified by their place of origin, colour, manufacturing method, surface texture, use and size.**

4. **B: There can be more than one frog in a brick provided they do not exceed 20 per cent of the volume of the brick.**

5. **Ratio for a lime mortar mix = 6 parts sand, 1 part lime and 1 part cement.**

CHAPTER 3

1. **A: You should never build in front of the building line.**

2. **B: With this amount of excavating, it would take too long to do manually, adding time and therefore cost to the project.**

3. **C: Profile boards should be set well away from the planned excavations to allow sufficient working space. This is particularly important if mechanical equipment is needed to carry out the excavation.**

4. **B: After placing the concrete in the foundations you need to remove the trapped air found in the voids of the concrete while it is still in a workable condition. If you don't carry out this step it could lead to the strength of the concrete being reduced.**

5. **C: To check that two lines are at 90° to each other you can use the 3:4:5 equation.**

CHAPTER 4

1. **B: The compressive force from the wall above is transmitted through the foundation at 45° to the vertical.**

2.

Brick term	Description	Figure
Type of bond	Patterns of brickwork used for structural and decorative purposes.	
Bat	Bricks cut widthways, available in quarters, halves or three quarters.	
Quoin	External angle on the outside of a wall at the corner of a building.	
Closer	Bricks cut lengthways at different angles, available in king, queen, bevelled and mitred.	

3. **C: The oversite concrete should be at least 100mm thick.**

4. **You can have the following foundation types: pad foundation, strip foundation, wide strip foundation, step strip foundation, narrow strip foundation.**

5. **A: The DPC should be positioned a minimum of 150mm above ground level.**

CHAPTER 5

1. **A & C: Dry bonding allows the bricklayer to create a balanced appearance of brickwork and avoid broken perpends throughout the height of the wall.**

2.

Flush	
Half-round tooled	
Raked or square recessed	
Weatherstruck	

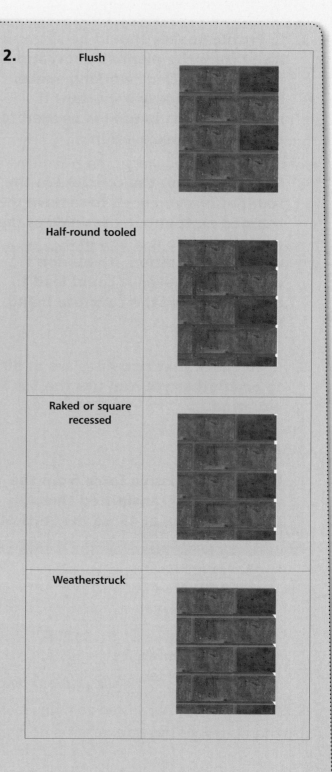

3. **False: Block internal walls can either be of solid or cavity construction.**

4. **Gauge, level, plumb, straight.**

5. **B: Joints should have been raked out to a depth of between 15 and 20 mm before repointing.**

CHAPTER 6

Please check your answers against the following. If any of the questions you answered are incorrect you are advised to go back to that section in the workbook or the e-learning programme to re-study.

Question 1
A, B and D.

Question 2
2000mm.

To calculate the actual measurement from the scale drawing you multiply the scale measurement by the scale ratio, in this case 100 × 20 = 2000mm.

Question 3
C: The usual percentage waste amount added is 5–10 per cent.

Question 4
189.

We need 60 bricks per m² of wall = 3 × 60 = 180.

To calculate 5 per cent waste = 180 × 0.05 (or 5 per cent) = 9.

Total bricks = 180 + 9 = 189.

Question 5
B: The UK construction industry sends 36 million tonnes of waste to landfill each year.

Question 6
C: The building line of a project will have been set by the local authority as part of the planning permission granted to a site.

Question 7
B: The curing for horizontal surfaces is approximately 7 days.

Question 8
B: The forces should spread through the foundation at a 45° angle to evenly distribute the loads from the wall above.

Question 9

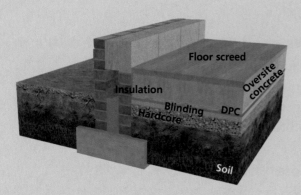

Layers of a solid ground floor

1: Hardcore

2: Blinding

3: DPC membrane

4: Insulation

5: Oversite concrete

6: Floor screed

Question 10
B: The usual practice is to dry bond the bricks from one end of the wall.

Question 11
C: Perpends are the position of the vertical joints in brickwork.

Question 12

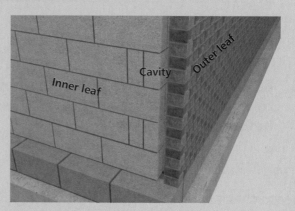

1: Inner leaf

2: Cavity

3: Outer leaf

Question 13
A: The cavity in a wall should be at least 50 mm.

Question 14
B: A wall tie should be positioned either sloping towards the outside wall or level.

Question 15
B: Partial fill insulation is float to the inner leaf of the wall.

Question 16
B: Pointing may be carried out on new builds where the mortar is to be a different colour to contrast with the brickwork.

Question 17

B: If doors and windows are to be fitted at a later date a dummy frame called a profile is used.

Question 18

C: A lintel is exposed to compressive forces from above and tensile forces from below.

Question 19

B: The gable end of a wall is constructed once the wall has reached the height of the wall plate and the roof trusses have been finished.

Question 20

B, C, E and F: Checks that should be carried out during bricklaying include gauge, level, plumb and straight.

Glossary

3:4:5 Equation A traditional method of checking ranging lines attached to the profile boards are at right angles to each other. For example, if line a–b is 3 cm, and line b–c is 4 cm, then line a–c should be 5 cm.

Accelerator An additive that speeds up the hydration of cement producing a higher strength at an earlier stage which reduces the setting time.

Additives A range of substances that can be added to mixtures to improve the strength of the mix or to control the timing in achieving the desired mix.

Aggregate The name given to the range of particulates used in construction. These can include sand, gravel and crushed stone.

Air vent Vents that can be built into a cavity wall below ground and above ground. Below ground they provide air where a hollow floor, normally of a timber construction, needs to be ventilated. Above ground they are built into the cavity where additional ventilation is needed in a room. Air vents bridge the cavity as a continuous duct to join the inlet and outlet of the openings.

Arris The edges of a brick.

Asbestos A fibrous mineral commonly used in buildings as fireproofing material until the mid 1980s. Can be a health hazard and should not be disturbed. Specialist advice must be sought if found or suspected.

Back line One of the lines attached to the profile boards during the setting out process of a building. The back line represents the back wall of the building.

Bat Part of a brick when cut square across its width. Bats cut as a quarter, half, or three quarters of the brick length are used to achieve a variety of bonding arrangements. A cut brick is any other length, cut from the whole brick, which is used to fit required wall dimensions.

Bed The under surface of a brick.

Bevelled closer A type of closer brick with a bevel along its length reducing a header at one end to 56 mm.

Blinding A layer of compacted sand on top of a hardcore bed before the damp proof membrane (DPM) is laid.

Block The most common block type is aggregate concrete blocks. They have a large number of desirable properties including high sound and thermal insulation and excellent moisture, fire and frost resistance. They are strong, lightweight, easy to work with and easy to fix to. Blocks are manufactured in solid, hollow and cellular block forms and one type of block can be used in every situation on a site.

Blockwork Walls built of blocks as opposed to bricks, which may be used externally with a rendered finish, but more widely for the internal walls of cavity walls.

Bond The arrangement of bricks to prevent vertical joints in succeeding course to coincide. This increases the stability and load-bearing capacity of the wall. The most common bonds in bricklaying are: English, Flemish and Stretcher bonds. The type of bond used may be chosen for strength, cost or decorative appearance.

Brickwork A solid wall built of bricks, laid to bond and in mortar. Used to be the most common load bearing external wall construction. Mainly finished with fair faced bricks and pointed or rendered. Minimal maintenance required but as properties age partial or complete re-pointing or re-rendering respectively may become necessary.

British standards A set of standards to ensure the quality of goods and services.

Broken bond This occurs when brick sizes will not fit the designed wall length. This is a common situation and requires careful planning (i.e. dry bonding) for quality face work. Where there is a broken bond and bricks need to be cut, the cut bricks should be placed under window and door openings to minimize the number of courses with cut bricks, leaving the majority of the wall true to bond.

Building line One of the lines set by the local building authority. The building must not be constructed in front of this line.

Bullnose brick A type of cut brick. These may be single or double bullnose. Either one or two ends of the stretcher face will have a 56mm radius curve. The single bullnose is used on the edges of sills or steps and is flat to form a radius corner. The double bullnose is used on edge as a capping brick.

Cant brick A type of cut brick. These may be single or double bull cant. Either one or two ends of the stretcher face will have a 45° cut. The uses of these bricks are similar to those for bullnose bricks.

Cavity The gap between the internal and external walls of a building. Usually 50mm wide to increase the thermal insulation and weather resistance of the wall. The cavity must be kept clear and not bridged (except for wall ties and insulation). A damp proof course (DPC) must be provided around the perimeter of openings in cavity walls otherwise dampness can occur internally.

Cavity bat A type of cavity insulation made from mineral fibres treated with a water repellent. This type of cavity insulation is designed to fill the cavity and is installed during the construction of a new build.

Cavity board A type of cavity insulation made from polyurethane, fibre glass and polystyrene supplied as rigid boards. This type of cavity insulation is designed to partially fill the cavity and is installed during the construction of a new build.

Cavity closer An insulated plastic extrusion used to close off openings (e.g. windows and doors).

Cavity foam A type of cavity insulation made from expanded foam, granules or mineral wool fibres. This type of cavity insulation is designed to fill the cavity and is injected into the cavity after a wall is constructed. Generally used for existing buildings with cavity walls.

Cavity fill Lean mix concrete filling of cavity from top of foundations to ground level. Provided to make wall below ground level solid and withstand the lateral pressure exerted by the subsoil on either side of the wall and prevent wall caving in. This concrete must be kept 150mm below the horizontal damp proof course (DPC) to allow the cavity to extend below it.

Cavity insulation For new build the standard of thermal insulation for external walls, set by building regulations, requires a suitable insulating material to be fixed in the cavity. There are a number of products available, rigid or flexible, and these either partially or completely fill the cavity. For existing buildings with cavity walls, the insulation material is injected into and will completely fill the cavity.

Cement A grey or white powdery material made from chalk or limestone and clay. Cement is the most common binder in bricklaying mortar and works by hardening as a result of a chemical reaction when mixed with water.

Chariot Tool used in bricklaying for achieving a raked or squared recessed mortar joint.

Closer brick A brick cut lengthways to give a reduced width. Used where the appearance of a full brick is required but the depth of the brickwork will not accommodate a full width, such as where a pier is inserted into a wall. There are a number of types of closer bricks including king closer, queen closer, bevelled closer and mitred closer.

Course A row of bricks, concrete blocks, etc. in a wall.

Curing The method of preventing the loss of water in concrete foundations by slowing the chemical reaction of hydration as the strength of the concrete cannot be maximized if it is dried too quickly. Curing usually takes up to seven days and there are a number of ways concrete can be cured including covering with damp hessian or polythene sheets or spraying the concrete with a curing compound. However, during cold weather, the hessian should be dry to prevent frosting.

Damp proof course (DPC) A horizontal layer of impervious materials such as bituminous felt, asphalt, two courses of slate or two courses of engineering bricks. It is usually laid at 150 mm above ground level to prevent moisture rising. For walls subject to high compressive loads. It is also necessary to form an impervious barrier in cavity walls when bridging openings (e.g. doors and windows). Damp proof course is commonly known as DPC.

Damp proof membrane (DPM) A layer of plastic sheeting laid over the blinding sand above a hardcore of a modern building, to prevent moisture rising from the ground into the floor structure. For this layer to become fully effective, it should be connected to the damp proof course (DPC) in the surrounding walls. Damp proof membrane is commonly known as DPM.

Datum peg Square timber peg used to mark the height of the brickwork up to damp proof course (DPC) level.

Dermatitis A skin condition caused by direct skin contact with irritants (e.g. mortar mix) causing an allergic reaction.

Door threshold The board at the base of an external door, designed to ensure water runs away from the building.

DPC The standard and widely used abbreviation for damp proof course.

DPC tray A membrane located above openings (e.g. windows and doors). Any water that penetrates through the openings is drained down the DPC tray and expelled from the wall through weep holes.

DPM The standard and widely used abbreviation for damp proof membrane (see Damp proof membrane).

Dry bonding A brick or timber joint that is not bonded with mortar or adhesive.

Dummy frame A timber frame used whilst the wall is being built to temporarily indicate where openings (e.g. doors and windows) will be. The frame is slightly larger than the door or window to be fitted.

Engineering brick A strong and dense type of brick, impervious to water so ideal for use in damp areas.

External plinth A facing brick with a 45° chamfer on the header and stretcher faces used to reduce the thickness of a plinth by 56mm (quarter brick) per course.

Floor screed The final layer of concrete laid on top of the oversite concrete to level off. The floor screed is usually laid later on in the project.

Frenchman A tool made by craftsmen, usually from an old table knife. The end of the knife blade is used for weatherstruck joints by cutting surplus mortar from bed and cross joints.

Frog The depression in a brick, the purpose of which is to reduce the amount of clay used in manufacture and its weight. A brick may have two frogs but must not exceed 20 per cent of the net volume of the brick.

Frontage line One of the lines attached to the profile boards during the setting out process of a building. The frontage line represents the front wall of the building.

Gable The triangular upper part of a wall at the end of a ridged roof.

Gauge rod A timber batten long enough to reach one storey high, marked with the top of each course of bricks.

Hardcore Once the foundation brickwork and blockwork are complete a layer of hardcore, usually formed of broken bricks and gravel bed, is laid on top of the subsoil. Hardcore is the base layer of a solid ground floor. A layer of blinding sand will be laid on top of the hardcore afterwards.

Header face The end surface of a brick or block.

Hessian A coarse fabric used to cover the concrete foundations during the curing process.

Inner leaf The internal wall of a cavity construction which is commonly formed of blocks. If partial fill insulation cavity boards are used, they should be fixed to the inner leaf using special wall ties.

Jointer A tool used in bricklaying for achieving a half-round tooled mortar joint.

Jointing The process of finishing off mortar joints in brickwork or blockwork to waterproof the wall. Timing is crucial for jointing as the mortar may crumble if jointing is carried out after the mortar has dried.

Joist A beam that supports a ceiling or floor.

Joist hanger Metal slots installed to wall plates, rafters or existing joists to support a row of joists. Available in different sizes to accommodate different joists.

King closer A type of closer brick with a bevel cut with a diagonal cut at one header face.

Level The horizontal level of a surface or structure.

Levelling The process of using a spirit level to check and mark levels.

Lime A white or grayish-white, odorless solid made from calcium carbonate, limestone or oyster shells. Used in mortars, plasters and cements.

Lintel A horizontal beam of timber (old buildings), stone, concrete or steel (new buildings), spanning the openings (e.g. doors and windows) in a wall to support the structure above.

Load-bearing wall A wall which supports the structure of the building above. It should not be removed or altered without professional assistance.

Mortar A mixture of sand, cement (sometimes with lime and/or additives) and water, used to bond stones and bricks. Can be mixed by hand or mechanically on or off site.

Narrow strip foundation A type of foundation used where the amount of space required to build on top of the concrete strip would make the foundation wider than it needed to be for structural reasons. A narrow trench is excavated, filled with concrete and the bricklayer then begins to build from ground level rather than from in the trench itself.

Outer leaf The external wall of a cavity construction. The outer leaf wall is tied to the inner leaf using wall ties.

Oversite concrete A layer of concrete which is at least 100mm thick that is laid over the insulation in a solid ground floor. It is not necessary to trowel-finish this concrete as the floor screed to be laid will adhere better to a tamped surface.

Ordinary Portland Cement (OPC) The most common type of cement. Made from crushed limestone or clay mixed with water, which is then heated at very high temperatures and ground into a powder form.

Pad foundation A type of foundation where a block of concrete is used when there is a single load being transmitted down a brick pier, concrete column or steel stanchion. Predominantly used in commercial buildings, not domestic low level structures.

Perpends The position of the vertical joints in brickwork. It is essential that they continue vertically from the first course of bricks to the top of the brickwork and should be checked with a spirit level every four or five courses to make sure they are plumb.

Personal Protective Equipment (PPE) Depending on the type of work, there are different types of equipment specifically designed to protect your health and safety. Examples include gloves, safety boots, goggles and dust mask.

Planning permission Application to the local councils for land to be developed or addition/modification made to an existing property.

Plaster A white or pinkish mineral formed from heating gypsum at high temperatures. Plaster is used to protect and enhance the appearance of the surface as it provides a joint-less finish.

Plasticizer An additive that increases fluidity or plasticity of a mortar, cement paste or concrete mixture and reduces water content and drying times.

Plinth stretcher A facing brick with a 45° chamfer on the stretcher face used to reduce the thickness of a plinth by 56mm (quarter brick).

Plumb The vertical level of a surface or structure.

Pointing Finishing off mortar joints that have been raked out to a depth of between 15–20mm. Pointing can be carried out during construction to apply a different colour mortar to contrast the brickwork, or it can be part of a renovation project if existing mortar has deteriorated.

Pointing trowel A trowel used in bricklaying for achieving a weatherstruck mortar joint.

Profile boards Boards placed at the corners of a building to transfer the plan outline of a building onto the ground. They are held securely in place by square pegs and ranging lines are fixed to them to indicate the foundation, frontage line, right angle lines and back line.

PPE The standard and widely used abbreviation for Personal Protective Equipment.

Queen closer A type of closer brick with a cut on the centre line along its length to produce a 56mm closer. This type of brick is used in all quarter bonds to set the required lap and must be placed immediately after the quoin header and in no other position.

Quoin The external angle of a building at a corner of the building.

Ranging line Heavy duty line that is used for the initial setting out by attaching it to profile boards to mark the trench lines and the face of the walls.

Retarder An additive used to extend the setting time of a mortar mix.

Reveal The sides of door and window openings which should be identified when setting out the first and second course of bricks. This is to ensure that there are no unbroken perpends throughout the height of the wall.

Reverse bond An alternative to a broken bond. This bond is achieved by a stretcher brick at one end with a header at the other end on the same course.

Right angle line One of the lines attached to the profile boards during the setting out process of a building. The right angle lines are at 90° to the frontage line and extend beyond the length of the building. A builder's square or the 3:4:5 equation should be used to check that these lines are at right angles.

Roof truss The timber frame structure of a roof, usually factory made and delivered to site.

Sand Fine aggregate that is one of the raw ingredients for mixing mortar.

Setting out The process of marking out a plan on the ground of a site using profile line boards connected by ranging lines.

Spirit level A tool used to check true vertical and horizontal lines indicated by a bubble in spirit-filled vials.

Step foundation A type of foundation used on sloping sites to reduce the amount of excavation needed and avoid different settlement rates in different layers of the subsoil. Construction begins at the lowest point and the foundations overlap as they move up the slope. The overlap must be twice as thick as the step or foundation thickness, whichever is the largest.

Stretcher face The side surface of a brick or block.

Strip foundation A common type of foundation generally used for low to medium rise domestic and industrial buildings. It is made from a continuous concrete mass situated under the wall which must be a minimum of 150mm thick, with an equal projection each side of the wall of at least the same measurement.

Subsoil The soil immediately below the hardcore of a foundation.

Sustainable Materials that have been sourced by causing little or no damage to the environment.

Trowel A range of hand-held tools used for mix, apply and spread or remove materials. There are many different types of trowels for different purposes including bucket trowel, gauge trowel, notched trowel and pointing trowel.

U value A measurement of the rate of heat loss through a wall, roof or floor which should be as low as possible to reduce the energy consumption of the building.

uPVC A type of stable plastic used in the manufacture of double-glazed window frames, doors and cladding.

Wall plate A horizontal timber bedded in mortar on top of the wall. This provides the support ceiling joists, rafters and roof truss.

Wall ties Metal connectors built into cavity walls to provide a structural link between the inner and outer leaf of the wall. There are many different types of wall ties and some are specially designed for use with insulation materials.

Weep holes In some parts of an external wall, water can collect behind the internal face within the cavity tray above window and door openings. Draining of this water can be achieved by opening cross joints spaced at regular intervals and installing plastic ducts or vents to keep insects out of the cavity.

Wide strip foundation When strip foundation is unsuitable due to the subsoil a wide strip foundation is used. As the foundation gets wider it must also become deeper to avoid tensile stress. Where this is uneconomical, reinforcement is used.

Window cill The board at the external base of a window designed to ensure water runs away from the building.

Index

3:4:5 equation 54–5, 129

accelerator 26, 27, 129
additives 32, 129
aggregate 23, 129
    storage 46–7
air vent 41–2, 129
Approved Code of Practice (ACoP) 14
arris (bricklaying) 18, 129
asbestos 43, 129
assembly drawing 12

back line 57, 129
base lines 53–6
bats 74–5
    storage 48
bed 18, 129
bevelled closer 76, 129
blinding 87, 129
block 2, 129
block internal walls 110
block plan 9
blocks 23–4
    calculating quantities 24
    storage 47
    types 23
blockwork 97, 129
bond (bricklaying) 73, 129
bonding 73–8
    arrangements 78
    terminology 73–7
brick bat 74, 129
bricklayer
    role 2
    on site 6–7
bricks 18–22
    calculating quantities 21–2
    parts of a brick 18–19
    shape 19–20
    storage 47
    types 18
brickwork 73, 129–30
    corners 79–81

positioning DPCs 86
walls 81–3
working below ground 84–5
bridging openings 104–8
British Standards 8, 130
broken bond 94, 130
building design 5
building line 52, 130
bullnose brick 19, 130

calculating quantities
    blocks 24
    bricks 21–2
cant brick 19, 130
cavity 37, 130
cavity bat 38, 130
cavity board 39, 130
cavity closer 105, 130
cavity fill 97, 130
cavity foam 40, 130
cavity insulation 37, 130
cavity walls 37–42, 96–9
    above ground construction 99
    air vents 41–2
    below ground construction 97–8
    insulation materials 38–40
    introduction 96
    solid foundation blocks 98
    two walls of solid blocks 97–8
    wall ties 40–1
cement 26, 27, 130
    storage 46
chariot 101, 130
checks 113
cills 105
closer brick 76, 130
codes of practice 14
concreting 60–4
    compacting and levelling foundations 62
    curing 63–4
    placing 60–1

Construction Design and Management Regulations (2007) 15
corners
    erecting 80–1
    setting out 79
course 2, 131
cross section drawing 11
curing 63–4, 131
customer care 113

damp proof course (DPC) 29, 80, 84–5, 131
    positioning 86
damp proof membrane (DPM) 87, 131
datum peg 80, 131
dermatitis 36, 131
door openings 104
door threshold 105–6, 131
DPC see damp proof course
DPC tray 108, 131
DPM see damp proof membrane
drawings
    scale 8
    types 9–12
dry bonding 94–6, 131
dry mortar silos 34
dummy frame 104, 131

elevation drawing 11
engineering brick 80, 131
English bond 78, 131
excavation 59–60
external plinth 19, 131

Flemish bond 78, 131
floor screed 87, 131
flooring types 87–9
flush joints 101
foundations 68–73
    compacting and levelling 62
    introduction 68–70
    types 70–3

Frenchman 101, 131
frog 18, 131
frontage line 53, 132

gable 94, 132
gable end 112
gauge rod 113, 132

half-round tooled joints 101
hardcore 49, 132
header face 18, 132
health and safety
    asbestos 43
    bricks 25
    materials, tools and equipment
        36
    site access and maintenance 113
    working below ground 84
hessian 63, 132
hollow ground floors 89

inner leaf 39, 132
insulation materials 38–40
    storage 48
internal walls 110

jointer 101, 132
jointing 94, 100–2, 132
    types 100–1
joist 89, 132
joist hanger 94, 111, 132

king closer 76, 132

level 2, 132
levelling 62, 132
lime 27, 132
lintel 107, 132
load bearing wall 58, 132

mortar 26–35, 79, 132
    how to mix 29–34
    materials used 26–7
    mixes 28–9

narrow strip foundation 72–3, 132

OPC see Ordinary Portland Cement
ordering materials 43–5
    sourcing materials 43
    waste calculation 44
Ordinary Portland Cement (OPC)
    27, 132
outer leaf 96, 132
oversite concrete 87, 132

pad foundation 70–1, 133
perpends 95, 133
personal protective equipment
    (PPE) 3, 133
plan drawing 10
planning permission 2, 7–12, 133
    scale drawings 8
    types of drawing 9–12
    when to apply 7
plaster 46, 133
    storage 46
plasticizer 26, 27, 133
plinth stretcher 19, 133
plumb 2, 133
pointing 27, 103, 133
pointing trowel 101, 133
PPE see personal protective
    equipment
profile boards 56–7, 133
    positioning 56–7
    ranging lines 57

Queen closer 76, 133
quoin 75, 133

raked or square recessed joints 101
ranging line 52, 57, 133
regulations 15
retarder 26, 27, 133
reveal 95, 96, 133
reverse bond 95, 133
right angle line 54, 133
roof truss 112, 133

sand 26, 27, 133
scale drawings 8

setting out 52–64, 133
    base lines 53–6
    bond 94
    building line 52
    concreting 60–4
    corners 79
    excavation 59–60
    profile boards 56–8
    transferring dimensions 58
setting up lines 58–9
site analysis 6–7
site plan 9–10
skills 3
solid ground floors 87–8
sourcing materials 43
spirit level 79, 134
step foundation 72, 134
storage of materials 45–8
stretcher bond 78, 134
stretcher face 18, 134
strip foundation 71, 134
subsoil 68, 134
sustainability 43, 48, 49
sustainable 89, 134

thresholds 105
transferring dimensions 58
trowel 2, 134

U value 38, 134
uPVC 104, 134

wall plate 111, 134
wall ties 40–1, 134
    storage 48
walls 81–3
waste calculation 44
waste disposal 48–9
waste minimization 49
water 27
weatherstruck joints 101
weep holes 97, 134
wide strip foundation 71, 134
window cill 105–6, 134
window openings 104
working below ground 84–5
working drawings 9